Jocelyn Brooke was born in 1908 in Sandgate, Kent. An unspectacular career at Worcester College, Oxford was followed by ten years in the book and wine trades. After five years in the Royal Army Medical Corps he worked as a talks producer for the BBC. His first book, THE MILITARY ORCHID was published in 1948. His writings include a masterly and exhaustive study of the British Orchid and three neatly effective psychological novels. Jocelyn Brooke died in 1966.

PRIVATE VIEW

Four Portraits

by

Jocelyn Brooke

Robin Clark
London

First published in paperback by Robin Clark Ltd. 1989
27/29 Goodge Street
London W1P 1FD

First published by James Barrie 1954

British Library Cataloguing in Publication Data
Brooke, Jocelyn 1908–1966
Private View.
I. Title
823′.914 [F]
ISBN 0-86072-123-X

Printed and bound in Great Britain by
Cox & Wyman Ltd, Reading, Berks

'To C. J. and Julia Greenwood

AUTHOR'S NOTE

Kurt Schlegel was first conceived and delivered—in a very much shortened form—as a broadcast talk; acknowledgements are therefore due to the British Broadcasting Corporation for permission to reproduce certain of the original passages; also to the editor of *The London Magazine*, in whose pages *Miss Wimpole* first appeared.

J. B.

Contents

Alison Vyse

Aᴛ the age of six I was, like most normally constituted children, a polymorphous pervert. True, the main stream of my libido was concentrated upon my nurse; but its tributary streamlets were apt to flow into some very queer channels; I cherished, for example, at one time, a hopeless (and undeclared) passion for my brother's friend Basil Medlicott—or, more accurately (since I had a marked tendency to fetishism), for his white flannel tennis-trousers; a passion which, I seem to remember, existed contemporaneously with a somewhat less romantic, more connubial affection for a black Pomeranian named Pompey, of impeccable pedigree but uncertain temper, who had been presented to me, as a birthday present, by Sir Squire and Lady Bancroft, neighbours of ours at Sandgate. Sometimes my romantic yearnings would take a less particularized, a more inclusive form—thus, for a period of some months, I became passionately obsessed by weasels, stoats, polecats and other animals of the same genus; their attraction for me was, I suppose, equivalent to that generic glamour which certain human categories—negresses, for example, or guardsmen—can exercise over the mind of an adult; nor was I happy until I had obtained a dead stoat which, when it had been stuffed by Mr Hesse, my taxidermist friend in Dover, I would insist on taking to bed with me.

I

Often enough, too, my affections would become involved with fictional characters—for instance, there was Peter, the circus-boy in *Stumps* (who now remembers that classic among Edwardian children's books?); there was also—for my heroes tended quite as often to be animal as human—Beatrix Potter's Mr Tod; and, above all (though this was at a slightly later date), Jack Martin, the heroic castaway of *Coral Island*, who became, for me, the hero-to-end-all-heroes, with whom I would identify many of the people who attracted me in real life. I remained faithful to Jack Martin for some considerable time, and no wonder; for Jack was a glamour-boy if ever there was one—'tall, strapping, broad-shouldered,' with a 'handsome, good-humoured, firm face.' Nor was he deficient in moral qualities—he 'had had a good education, was clever and hearty and lion-like in his actions, but mild and quiet in disposition.' He cherished, moreover, a 'peculiar fondness' for the narrator, Ralph Rover, with whom, of course (for Ralph was a somewhat priggish and stupid youth), I identified myself.

I must, I suppose, have been approaching my sixth birthday when these diffuse and impermanent Transformations of the Libido gave place to what, by contrast, might almost be classified as a Grand Passion. My new love was no doubt doomed, by its very nature, to be unrequited; but it did at least (being relatively extravert and heterosexual) mark a certain psychological advance upon my previous amours.

During the summer of that year, the girls of Gaudeamus, the somewhat 'advanced' school which my sister went to at Sandgate, gave a performance of *A Midsummer-night's Dream*. As a very special treat I was taken to this production which, in more ways than one, was to exercise a profound influence upon me. In the first place, it marked my initiation into the mysteries of the Drama: I had never been taken to a play before, though I had heard of such things from the grown-ups. This was thrilling enough, in itself; but my excitement was increased still further when I learned that, since the play did not begin till six o'clock in the evening, I should be allowed to sit up for two whole hours after my usual bedtime. My excitement was tempered, it is true, by an element of nervousness: for I had been told that I myself should be going next term to the Kindergarten (a prospect which I viewed with the utmost terror), and it seemed to me only too probable that the play was a mere ruse for luring me, prematurely, into the dreaded precincts of Gaudeamus. I made up my mind that, once inside, I would cling tightly to my nurse's hand, lest I should be seized upon by Miss Pinecoffin, the headmistress, and cast immediately into the horrifying depths of the 'Kindergarten'—a place which I visualized as a cross between a mediaeval dungeon and the witch's cottage in 'Hansel and Gretel'.

No such disaster did, in fact, occur: though certainly, on our arrival, it seemed imminent, for, no sooner had we entered the 'Hall', than I was forcibly parted from my nurse and made to sit on a hassock in the front row, among a crowd of little boys and girls who, as I afterwards discovered, were the actual inmates of that very Kindergarten which had inspired me with such terror. They didn't, as it happened, seem very terrifying or, for that matter, terrified: plainly they were not expecting to be fattened up and devoured, like the children in the fairy-story, by Miss Pinecoffin. Soon I regained my confidence; the curtain rose at last; and I found myself gazing, in a kind of bewildered ecstasy, at the spectacle upon the stage.

Goodness knows what I had expected—something very

glamorous and exciting, no doubt; I only know that, after the first ten minutes, I began to feel extremely bored. So this was a *play*! A lot of people dressed up in bath-towels, mouthing words which I couldn't understand. . . . I was bitterly disappointed; I almost wished that I were safely home again. Presently, however, the scene changed—'A wood near Athens', one of my grown-up neighbours in the row behind whispered to me informatively—and suddenly my interest was aroused. Puck made his first entrance; and, from being merely interested, I became enthusiastic: this was more like what I had expected—this, at last, was perhaps the real thing; what had gone before was, no doubt, a mere dull preamble which one endured to please the grown-ups—like eating bread-and-butter before cake.

The truth was, of course, that I had fallen head-over-heels in love. It was, quite literally, love at first sight: from the moment Puck made his (or rather her) entrance, I was completely enslaved. The part was taken, so my neighbour informed me, by a little girl called Alison—Alison Vyse. She must have played it, as I realize now, with the verve and distinction of a born actress; even then I could see that her performance, compared with that of the other little girls, was remarkable. Whereas the rest of the cast seemed merely to be going through a series of motions, Puck really 'lived' her part: she was like a 'real' person moving among a crowd of waxworks.

But it was not her performance so much as her personal appearance with which I was chiefly concerned. Plump-cheeked, tall for her age, with long, slender legs, she seemed to me the most beautiful person I had ever seen. Her hair, in particular, fascinated me, for she wore it 'bobbed'—a novelty in those days; the colour of ripe corn, it swung and rippled

4

about her head with the smooth motion of some water-plant stirred by the current of a stream.

I gazed upon her, entranced; when she was off-stage, I waited with an acute impatience for her next appearance; as the play drew to its close, my pleasure became tinged with an intolerable melancholy, as I realized that I should have to go home to bed without even exchanging a word with her. If only I had had the courage to step up on to the stage, and beg her to come home with me! She could not, I felt sure, refuse; nobody, it seemed to me, could resist such a passionate supplication as mine. I imagined myself bearing her home with me in my arms—reduced, for practical purposes, to the size of a rather large teddy-bear. Once at home, I would give her a supper of Patent Groats or Barley, the diet on which I was accustomed to feed my imaginary 'pets'; afterwards, I would shut her in the cage (also, alas, imaginary) in which, until recently, I had kept a captive soldier or sometimes, for a change, an airman of the Royal Flying Corps. On second thoughts, however, I decided that I would take her to bed with me—an honour which, up till now, had been accorded only to the stuffed stoat and to one or two other very special favourites.

At last the play was over. I was hurried away, for it was long past my bedtime, and I was liable, on such occasions, to get 'overtired'. In a daze, I climbed the hill to our house; the late June sunlight, striking through the hedges of tamarisk, dazzled my eyes, so that I stumbled as though I were drunk. Reaching home, I was led into the dining-room where, as the grand climax to this day of 'treats', I was to be allowed to partake of the grown-ups' Late Dinner—which consisted (so far as myself was concerned) of potatoes and gravy, with a few shoots of asparagus.

The western sun blazed through the french windows;

speechlessly, I allowed myself to be lifted into a chair; the potatoes and asparagus made their appearance. . . . But I could only stare sightlessly before me, bewildered by the unaccustomed atmosphere of conviviality, and consumed already by a desolating nostalgia for the glories of the 'play', and for the corn-gold hair and plump cheeks of Alison Vyse.

Not even the asparagus could tempt me. I heard the grown-ups whispering among themselves, and caught the words 'overexcitement . . . overtired . . . '. Soon I was taken up to bed; and for once I made no objection—for all I wanted was to be left alone, to brood in peace upon the wonders of the evening, and upon my new-found love. 'Overtired', I heard my nurse murmur, once again, on the way upstairs; and this time I did, mildly, protest.

'I'm *not* "overtired",' I said.

'Oh yes you are,' she retorted, firmly.

'I'm not, I'm *not*,' I insisted. And it was, to a great extent, true: for I was suffering, not so much from fatigue, as from the fact that I had, for the first time in my life, fallen passionately and hopelessly in love.

But I could hardly, after all, expect my nurse to realize this overwhelming fact; nor, for that matter, had I any inclination to make it public. Quiet and obedient, for once, I allowed myself to be undressed and put to bed; then, clasping the stuffed stoat firmly to my breast, lay quietly, for a long time, watching the summer twilight fade slowly behind the 'lilac'-patterned chintz curtains, and wishing that the stoat, whose hairy muzzle lay pressed against my own hot face, was not a stoat at all, but a little girl with corn-coloured hair called Alison Vyse.

For the next few weeks Alison possessed my heart entirely;

6

night after night I would lie awake, remembering her plump rosy face beneath its swinging bell of hair, and weaving elaborate phantasies in which we shared a whole series of improbable and romantic adventures. I liked to imagine that my parents had adopted her, and that she was to make her home with us for the rest of her life; for this purpose, I ruthlessly killed off her entire family, and one of my favourite phantasies consisted in consoling poor Alison, with endless embraces and tender words, for her tragic bereavement. In sober fact (as I had learned), she lived with a large family of relations at Hythe; my parents were acquainted with them, and, had I been more enterprising, I could, no doubt, have engineered a meeting; but I was far too timid and reticent to suggest such a thing, and indeed it scarcely even occurred to me. Like my other attachments, my love for Alison nourished itself almost entirely on phantasy; and I was content, I think, that it should continue to do so. If I had suddenly found myself in her company I should, I am certain, have been much too terrified to declare my love, or even to have been ordinarily polite; for I suffered from an almost pathological fear of other children, more especially when they happened to be of the female sex.

Yet her image haunted me perpetually: again and again I would rehearse, in my imagination, the scenes of the play in which she had appeared; I even, with a considerable effort, stumbled through the text of *A Midsummer-night's Dream* in the big, three-volume Shakespeare which I had recently acquired. Like all lovers I felt, at times, an ungovernable desire to talk about my love; and I would contrive, by a number of cunning devices, to drag her name into the conversation whenever opportunity offered. The easiest approach, naturally, was by way of Shakespeare, and I think that my family, at this time, were genuinely hoodwinked into believing that I was something of an infant prodigy, with a precocious passion for 'literature'. Needless to say, I was nothing of the sort; but I had no intention of confessing to my parents the real reason for this sudden interest in late Renaissance comedy.

With Ninnie (as I called my nurse), I was somewhat less reticent: I would discuss Alison with her quite openly, though I was rather careful to maintain the polite fiction that it was, merely, her performance in the part of Puck which I had really admired. Yes, Ninnie would agree, she had been 'very good' —you could see that she was a 'born actress'; how well she had danced, and how prettily she had spoken her final speech, etc. etc. Not surprisingly, I found such comments inadequate: what I really wanted was not so much dramatic criticism as personal gossip. But Ninnie, alas, knew very little more about Alison's private life than I did myself; and I was soon thrown back, once again, on my phantasies. I invented a 'wild' Alison, who inhabited the thickets of tamarisk under the cliff, which I had already peopled with a number of other phantastic figures. In the 'wild' state she became, I found, more manageable, I felt that I had more power over her; and sometimes, in my more malicious moods, I could 'punish' her for a number of imaginary misdeeds.

Yet there was, as I dimly realized, something sterile and unsatisfying about such a relationship; and I began to yearn for some more dynamic expression of my love, some means by which (without actually making Alison's acquaintance) I could create a visible and tangible image of that plump seductive body and that corn-coloured bell of hair.

I resorted, at last, to an expedient which, on several previous occasions, had helped to assuage my amorous pangs: I decided to make a 'stuffed' Alison. I had already, with Ninnie's help, manufactured a very creditable airman, who, like the stuffed stoat, had been my chosen bedfellow for a few weeks, and had, as such, given me considerable satisfaction. True, he wasn't a 'real' airman, whereas the stoat, though stuffed, was a genuine stoat; but he had served his purpose, up to a point, and I decided that Alison, too, should be immediately incarnated in this tangible, if somewhat unsatisfactory, form.

I duly consulted with Ninnie—being careful, of course, to imply that what I wanted was merely a 'stuffed' edition of Puck, not of the actress whom I happened (quite by chance) to have seen in the part. Alison herself, I am afraid, would hardly have been flattered by the curious *Doppelgänger* which resulted from Ninnie's painstaking efforts; the coarse linen 'body', stuffed with cotton-wool and snippets, bulged in the wrong places; the boot-button eyes leered in a most unsuitable manner; the yellow floss-silk which represented Alison's 'bobbed' hair suggested nothing so much as an albino golliwog. Still, I was satisfied—at least, for the time being; and, on the night of its completion, I took my Pygmalion-image to bed with me, and hugged it to my breast with a passion which was as genuine as my imagination could make it.

Like the stuffed airman, my new bedfellow proved satisfactory enough—up to a point; but I continued, none the less, to yearn hopelessly for the 'real' Alison. Her name, especially, haunted me, repeating itself over and over again in my mind like an incantation; in this she differed from her predecessor of the R.F.C. who, poor fellow, had never had a name at all, for I had, at the time, been in love, not so much with one particular airman, as with the whole Flying Corps *en masse*. Alison. . . . The name became associated, in my mind, with the alyssum which, in April, covered the rockery in our garden with its festoons of vivid purple; and in consequence the image of Alison herself would present itself to me, henceforward, against a background of spring flowers and foliage, an incarnation of that season which I loved above all others, and to which I would look forward, throughout the year, with an almost unbearable impatience.

At the beginning of the autumn term I began to go to the Kindergarten at Gaudeamus. I was agreeably surprised to find that this institution was by no means the Udolpho which I had anticipated; Miss Pinecoffin, though stern in her demeanour, showed no signs of wishing to devour me; yet I was but ill-adapted, by temperament, for communal life, and, though I encountered none of the Gothic horrors I had expected, I lived in a perpetual tremor of nervousness—afraid of being late, afraid of being laughed at, afraid, above all, that Ninnie might one day forget to call for me at half-past twelve, and that I should be faced by the appalling prospect of eating my midday dinner in the school dining-hall, among a tittering crowd of little girls.

My terrors were, at first, somewhat mitigated by the thought that I should be able to feast my eyes, every day of my life, upon the 'real' Alison Vyse; but alas! my hopes were to be largely disappointed, for Alison must have been two or three years older than myself, and, at Morning Prayers—the only occasion on which I was likely to see her—she stood far away from me in one of the back rows. By screwing my head round, I could occasionally catch a glimpse of her blonde bob and her pink, peach-bloomed cheeks; and on one or two occasions I encountered her, briefly, in the mid-morning break—she would rush past me, her hair flying, a pile of books under her arm, and without a glance to spare for anybody as obscure as myself. She seemed, indeed, whenever I saw her, to be in a hurry: a quality which, for that matter, she shared with most of the other girls, for life at Gaudeamus appeared to be lived perpetually 'against time'—people rushed to and fro with a hurried and purposeful air, as though their simplest actions were fraught with a world-shaking importance.

On the whole, though, I was fairly happy at school: as always, I was hopeless at Arithmetic (which, in the Kindergarten, was rather artily called 'Numbers'), but I could read fluently and well for my age, and at the weekly 'Nature' class I scored a distinct success by bringing my stuffed stoat to school with me. The stoat was much admired and was even (somewhat to my alarm) borrowed by one of the other forms; I liked to imagine, when it was at last returned to me, that it had perhaps been actually handled by Alison Vyse herself.

The term wore on: I made a raffia table-napkin ring, to present to my mother at Christmas; and, though I continued to find the tempo of life rather too arduous, I managed, after a fashion, to adapt myself. I was not, I realized, like other little boys (of whom there were several, besides myself, in the Kindergarten); I was too timid, too self-effacing, I liked all the wrong things—trains, for instance, bored me, and I was a muff at all games. I cherished, in secret, a passionate admiration for a little boy called Stephen, who had the reputation for being very naughty: he would fidget through the morning classes, tease the girls in the break, and, in general, make a thorough nuisance of himself. Yet, naughty as he was, I knew that Miss Prendergast—who taught the Kindergarten—preferred Stephen to myself. I wished that I had the courage to be as naughty as he; but somehow, whenever I made a deliberate attempt to misbehave, it didn't quite come off. I suppose I was too half-hearted about it; on the whole, I decided, it was more comfortable to be law-abiding—I lacked the capacity, so it seemed, for sinning in the grand manner.

Our garden at Sandgate descended in a series of terraces to the beach; these, for the most part, were laid out with flower-beds and separated, one from another, by low walls of rough stone-work, planted with wallflowers and rock-plants. Between the first and second terraces, however, there was a short, steep slope, overhung by a canopy of laurustinus and tamarisk, and generally referred to, by my family, as 'The Bushes'. Dark, gloomy, and for the most part unvisited by the grown-ups, the Bushes had for me a peculiar fascination: one could almost fancy oneself in a real wood, and I made several attempts to naturalize my favourite wild-flowers in the loose, sandy earth. An Early Purple Orchid, imported from the woods of the Elham Valley, did raise my hopes by putting up a leaf or two for several years running; but it never produced a flower-spike, and I soon became discouraged. The soil in the Bushes was no doubt too poor, and the shade too deep, to nourish anything but the periwinkles, which sprawled in luxuriant masses along the bottom of the little slope.

During the autumn in which I began first to go to the Kindergarten, I spent much of my time, when I was not at school, pottering about the Bushes, which, more than ever, became for me a sort of bolt-hole into which I could escape from the importunities of the grown-ups, and in which, too, I felt at a safe remove from the unnerving complexity of my new life at Gaudeamus. In the Bushes, in fact, I could (as they say) retire into my phantasy-life, and was able successfully to forget that such people as Miss Pinecoffin and Miss Prendergast had ever existed.

In the mild October afternoons I would take myself off to the gloomy little shrubbery, on the plea of having 'work' to do (this, I had noticed, was the term most frequently employed

by the grown-ups when they wished to be by themselves);
once arrived in the Bushes, however, I would, as often as not,
neglect my somewhat hypothetical labours, and would content myself by perching upon the low bough of a tamarisk
which projected conveniently into mid-air, and from which
I could look down (with a rather thrilling sense of being
enskied among the tree-tops) upon the terrace below and
upon the distant prospect of the sea. The branch, resilient
though perfectly solid, formed a kind of swing, and I would
sit here, for an hour at a time, imagining myself a cowboy
cantering across boundless prairies, or a sailor perched on the
crow's nest of some schooner in the South Seas. In the garden
below, the late Michaelmas daisies smouldered with a subdued
brilliance of crimson and smoky blue; from the edge of the
beach, below the bottom terrace, rose a drift of bonfire-smoke,
its sharp, astringent odour mingled with the salty tang of
sea-weed; gulls circled with far, melancholy cries above my
head, and from the misty distances of the channel came the
dull, iterated note of a fog-horn, far out towards Dungeness.

At such moments, I would experience a curious mingling
of sadness and a vague, romantic excitement; sometimes I was
content to remain passive during these visitations, more often
my emotion would demand some kind of expression, and I
would feel impelled to give it permanent form in what I was
wont to describe to myself, somewhat inaccurately, as a 'story'.
These 'stories' were, in fact, not so much stories as poems, and
on the infrequent occasions when I managed to commit them
to paper, consisted, as often as not, of a kind of invocatory
prose-poetry addressed, usually, to my stuffed stoat, or to
some other hero or heroine of the moment. Alison Vyse,
needless to say, inspired a number of these essays in *vers libres*,
which, in retrospect, seem to have been written somewhat in

the style of Walt Whitman, with side-glances at the later work of Jules Laforgue. At one time I even conceived a kind of poetic drama (a form which, I may say, I have never attempted since) in which Alison was the heroine; the other characters being, I think, mainly 'wild' airmen and various representatives of the weasel tribe.

My efforts to make a garden in the Bushes had proved, as I have said, unsuccessful; and, since I couldn't grow flowers there, I tended more and more, during those autumn afternoons, to concentrate upon my literary activities. Sometimes, however—for I possessed a distinctly Tolstoyish streak—I would feel the need for a spell of manual labour; and on such occasions I would occupy myself with the construction of what I was wont to call, with deliberate indefiniteness, a 'place'.

These 'places' (for there were a series of them) represented, I can only suppose, an attempt to impose upon the inchoate waste land of the Bushes a local habitation and a name. My project of a garden having proved abortive, I was worried by the amorphous, uncivilized quality of my chosen haunt: the Bushes, unlike the rest of the garden, seemed to possess no particular meaning or purpose, they existed, so to speak, *in vacuo*, a mere no-man's-land between the flower-beds above and the shingle-floored terrace (which we called the quarter-deck) below. I determined, therefore, to introduce some kind of order into this unsatisfactory wilderness; since, however, I was anxious to preserve the Bushes as my own private domain, it was important to do nothing which might attract the notice of the grown-ups. Thus, I had at one time conceived the idea of digging out a level platform, large enough to accommodate a deck-chair and, perhaps, a small table; this plan however was, somewhat reluctantly, abandoned, for it seemed only too likely that such a pleasant arbour might

become popular, with the rest of the family, as a place in
which to 'sit-out' on hot summer afternoons.

Instead, I began to construct a series of smaller platforms,
shoring them up with old seed-boxes, discarded tins and so on;
here and there I would hollow out a small cave, in which I
would place a toy motor-car or aeroplane or (on occasions
when I wanted to 'punish' them) one or another of my various
'pets'; the stuffed airman, for instance, would quite often find
himself condemned, for one reason or another, to a spell of
confinement-to-barracks, and even Alison herself—for whom
my love had lately taken on a slightly sadistic tinge—was on
more than one occasion accorded the same treatment.

The building of these 'places' kept me happily occupied for
some weeks; but in due course, as was to be expected, my
secret was discovered by the grown-ups who, plainly mysti-
fied by these curious and apparently pointless constructions,
proceeded (like visitors to an exhibition of abstract pictures)
to advance a number of ingenious theories as to what, exactly,
they were 'meant to be'.

'Why, there's a road—and there's a garage' (pointing to
one of the toy motors) 'and surely that's a house'. . . . Like
some pioneer of Cubism, I would listen, with a supercilious
disdain, to their fatuous comments: outwardly calm, but
inwardly enraged by such attempts to translate my essays in
Significant Form into the humdrum terms of mere academic
realism. Occasionally, in the face of some more than usually
Philistine approach, I would be moved to protest—as, for
instance, when some gushing lady visitor proclaimed, trium-
phantly, that what I was trying to make must be a 'little fort'
(it was in the days when toy forts were fashionable, and I had
in fact introduced, into one of my abstract compositions, a
few lead soldiers).

'It's *not* a fort,' I exclaimed, furiously, 'it's a *place*.' Then, aware that my tone had passed the bounds of decorum, and that I had been betrayed into the unforgivable crime of being-rude-to-a-visitor, I rushed up to the nursery, where I tried to explain to Ninnie, all over again, that my 'places' were *not* forts but, merely, Places. Ninnie, it must be admitted, showed a certain sympathy—she did not, as it happened, like this particular lady—but even she must have found it difficult, I imagine, to appreciate the aesthetic and philosophic subtleties which so painfully preoccupied me.

November came, and, with the autumn rains, my carefully-constructed 'places' gradually disintegrated, tumbling bit by bit down the slope into the thicket of periwinkle below. I was not, as it happened, particularly worried by this melancholy *dégringolade*, for I wasn't allowed, in any case, to play in the Bushes during the winter. With a peculiar heartlessness, I had abandoned my stuffed airman to his fate, and not only the airman but (worse still) the bulging, yellow-haired *Doppelgänger* who had represented for me, however inadequately, the plump, adorable form of Alison Vyse. Poor Alison, I suppose, had been—at the time of my last visit to the Bushes —undergoing (like the airman) one of her spells of solitary confinement; concealed, along with the toy motor, in the little cave, she mouldered gradually away throughout the winter, and, by the time I revisited, in April, the ruins of my 'place', had become quite unrecognizable. This sad fact, far from depressing me, gave me, I am sorry to say, a certain satisfaction; for it seemed to me that, by destroying the image of my former love, I had finally purged myself of the emotion itself. If I had been acquainted with the practices of mediaeval witchcraft, I might even have cherished a malicious hope that the real, flesh-and-blood Alison was by now prostrated with some hideous and wasting disease; I did not, however, carry my theories of sympathetic magic quite so far as this—I was content to know that my love for Alison had at last died a natural death, and that I was heart-free once again.

This process had, no doubt, been speeded-up by the fact that Alison herself had left Gaudeamus at the end of the spring term, and been sent to a boarding-school near Brighton, where, far from being moribund, she was perfectly well and, so it appeared, extremely happy. This interesting piece of information I heard—or rather overheard—from a girl at Gaudeamus who had once been Alison's special chum; I received it without emotion, feeling, indeed, a certain relief in the knowledge that I should never, in all probability, see Alison again. To encounter her now, so long after I had ceased to love her, could only, I thought, lead to embarrassment; it had been quite bad enough to rediscover her rotted and faceless image in the Bushes, and to meet her in the flesh would be, I felt, infinitely worse.

I did not, however, remain fancy-free for long. During the Easter holidays, we went for a fortnight to our country-cottage in the Elham Valley; and here I proceeded to fall in love all over again—this time with the young man who delivered our bread from the baker's in the next village. He was a dark, handsome fellow, and wore a cloth cap and a very smart pair of riding breeches; his name was Mr Bilham. Every morning I would wait outside our front garden for the appearance of his pony and trap; in due course, he would come spanking along the village-street, cracking his whip, and calling greetings to the cottagers as he passed. When he smiled, his teeth flashed very white in his brown, swarthy face; probably he had a streak of gipsy blood.

Towards myself he showed a jovial, avuncular affection:
he would greet me with the same slightly roguish, devil-may-
care manner with which he hailed the village-girls—this, in
itself, was thrilling enough—and would then stop to chat for
a few minutes, allowing me to pat his pony, and even, on one
delirious occasion, to mount into the driver's seat. He was, in
fact, extremely kind to me, and I ought, I suppose, to have
been satisfied. But I wasn't; the brief morning colloquies left
me with a sense of intolerable frustration—I looked forward,
for the rest of the day (and for a considerable part of the night),
to next morning's visit. I should have liked Mr Bilham to
come and live with us permanently; nothing, indeed, would
have satisfied me but to have him by my side all day, and to
take him, like the stuffed airman, to bed with me as well.

Plainly this was impossible: one couldn't have bakers' boys
coming to live with one for the asking, and, even if this had
been possible, I was sure that my family would not have
allowed me to take Mr Bilham to bed with me; for that
matter, Mr Bilham himself might have raised objections—
indeed, by the end of our brief visit, he already showed signs
of being a little bored by my daily importunities, and I
realized, as so often before, that my love was doomed to be
unrequited.

I was depressed, for more reasons than one, by our return
to Sandgate: for one thing, my family had, contrary to their
usual custom, let the cottage for August and September, so
that we should be remaining at Sandgate for the whole of the
summer holidays. This was bad enough, in itself; but the
dismal prospect was made yet more melancholy for me by the
thought that I should be parted indefinitely from Mr Bilham.
Probably we should not return to the cottage till next spring
—perhaps not even then; by that time, anything might have

happened—Mr Bilham might have died, or left the district, or the world might have come to an end. Nor was this all; for, to these horrific visions of the future, was added the certain knowledge that, in the autumn term, I should be going to a preparatory school at Folkestone, a fate to which I looked forward with unmitigated horror.

However, for the time being—for the summer term, that is to say—I was to remain at Gaudeamus. By now, I had succeeded in adapting myself, with moderate success, to the hectic and nerve-racking life of the Kindergarten; I continued to manufacture raffia mats and napkin-rings with a kind of neurotic intensity, dimly aware that this peculiar and apparently useless occupation formed a part of some important ritual, to whose true and central nature I had not the slightest clue. I sighed for our summer cottage, and for Mr Bilham; consoling myself, in a rather half-hearted way, by an entirely platonic passion for one of the mistresses who took the higher forms in Mathematics and French. I never spoke to this lady, and the only occasions on which I caught a glimpse of her were at Morning Prayers, when I would watch her lustily singing, her head held back like that of a chicken in the act of drinking; as she sang, a large protuberant gland in her throat bobbed up and down with such violence that I expected, every moment, to see it jump out of her mouth and drop upon the long table behind which, with the assembled staff, she was standing.

The long summer term came to an end at last, and, since we were not to go to the cottage, I settled down to enjoy such compensations as offered themselves. In the afternoons I would retreat, as often as not, to the Bushes, where I would occupy myself with the construction of a new series of 'places'; or, perched comfortably on the swinging tamarisk bough, I would brood unhappily upon the dreary prospect

of the future, which I envisaged as a world of perpetual
'school', from which I should seldom—perhaps never—escape,
and in which my beloved Mr Bilham, with his gay smile and
his riding breeches, could have, alas, no part whatsoever. I
did attempt to make a 'stuffed' Mr Bilham, but had little
success, for I was too shy to ask Ninnie to assist me; the
R.F.C.—and even Alison Vyse—were all very well, but to
include Mr Bilham in my pantheon of sacred images would
not, I felt instinctively, meet with the approval of the grown-
ups, who possessed, as I very well knew, inexplicable prejudices in such matters.

One day, during the first week of the holidays, I returned
from my usual morning walk to be greeted by a shattering
piece of news. A little girl was coming to stay with us: she
was two or three years older than I, but was rather lonely (her
parents, it seemed, were much abroad), so would probably
be quite pleased to have a little boy to play with. I was adjured
to be on my best behaviour, and to be especially kind to her,
as she would, no doubt, be feeling rather homesick.

'Just think,' said the grown-ups, 'just think what it would
be like if *you* had to spend the holidays in someone else's
home, and far away from Daddy and Mummy.'

I received the news with a disgust only slightly mitigated
by the fact that it was a little girl, not a boy, who was coming
to stay. Girls, after all, though they might be senior to me in
age, were admittedly of an inferior breed; they were not in a
position, as boys were, to laugh at my defects—at my thin
legs, my badness at games and my general effeminacy. Quite
recently, a little boy of my own age, called Dennis, had come
to tea, and had insisted on jumping over the edge of the lawn
on to the sloping path below—a height of some five feet. He
had dared me to do the same; but alas, my courage had failed

me, and I had slunk away, pursued by Dennis's unkind taunts, to the nursery, where I pretended that I had a headache, and was duly put to bed and dosed with liquorice-powder. The memory of this episode still painfully rankled; I had for some time now cherished a secret ambition to be a soldier when I grew up, and I realized, only too well, that my conduct, in evading the ordeal-by-jumping, had been anything but soldierly. I hoped, devoutly, that the little girl who was coming to stay would not want to jump off walls; little girls, on the whole, were not given to such odious habits; and even supposing that this particular little girl wished to amuse herself by jumping off the edge of the lawn, she could, I thought, be safely left to do so by herself, without too much loss of face on my part. Soon, however, a worse possibility struck me: perhaps she would want to bathe, and insist upon my bathing with her! My stomach turned over, my mouth went dry. I lived, during the summer months, in perpetual terror of being made to bathe; and it seemed only too probable that, in my capacity as host to the unknown little girl, I should be required to do so in her company.

'Perhaps you know the little girl already,' my mother continued. 'She was at Gaudeamus for a time—she left at the end of the Easter term, I think. Such a nice little thing: her name's Alison, by the way—Alison Vyse.'

The incredible truth dawned upon me slowly: I thought at first that my mother must have made a mistake, or that perhaps there was another little girl called Alison Vyse. . . . But there was, as I soon discovered, no doubt about the identity of our visitor: 'such a *clever* little actress,' I heard the grown-ups saying, 'she was Puck, you know, in *A Midsummer-night's Dream*. The Drake-Connollys think the poor mite may really have talent.'

I wondered why Alison should be referred to as a 'poor mite': perhaps her parents had deserted her, I thought, or possibly she herself really was, in actual fact, suffering from some lingering and fatal illness, like her straw-stuffed image (which had by this time been relegated to the dustbin). I was soon to be enlightened: Alison's parents had not deserted her, but were in India; usually, as I already knew, she spent her holidays at Hythe, with her mother's family, the Drake-Connollys, with whom my parents were acquainted; this summer, however, the Drake-Connollys had Illness in the House—the phrase was uttered, whenever I was present, in impressive undertones, and with an air of shocked, respectful gravity, as though it were in some mysterious way connected with lavatories or babies (it happened, in fact, to be scarlet fever); Alison, therefore—who had been staying elsewhere since the end of her school-term, and was therefore not a 'contact'—had been invited to stay with us for a week or two until her grandmother's household should be out of quarantine.

I cursed the Fates for their tardiness, and for what seemed to me the gross inefficiency of their arrangements. (These Fates, for reasons best known to myself, I visualized as being incarnated in the two impoverished old dressmakers, named Hodsell, whom my mother patronized in Folkestone; dressed always in funereal black, and bent perpetually over vast sewing-machines—which bore the mysterious name of Pfaff—they seemed to me to embody, with a perfect appropriateness, the forces of a malign Destiny.) I cursed the Fates: why could they not have arranged for Alison to visit us before? A few months ago (but it seemed to me, by now, to be half a lifetime), a mere five minutes spent in her company would have been enough to make me deliriously happy; and now she was coming to us—the real, the authentic Alison Vyse—

for a whole week or more! During this time I should have her to myself—to talk to and play with as much as I liked; and it would all, alas, be of no avail—for I was no longer in love with her.

The Miss Hodsells, it seemed to me, had been playing a number of shabby tricks just lately. Who but these unkind Fates (with the aid, no doubt, of their enormous and sinister 'Pfaffs') could have impelled my family to let the cottage for the summer, just at the very moment when I had lost my heart to Mr Bilham? And now, in their hard, Pfaffish way, they had ordained that Alison, with whom I was no longer in love, must come to spend the summer with us. . . . In after years, when I encountered the phrase 'The Irony of Fate', I realized its meaning only too well; and indeed there was, about this visit of Alison's, a kind of ironic fatality which I was to recognize, at a later date, in the works of Proust and of Thomas Hardy. It was, in fact, my first experience of that psychological law with whose workings, in after life, I was to become familiar enough—the law, I mean, which decrees that Desire and Opportunity shall never (or only in extremely rare and exceptional circumstances) coincide.

I sighed, afresh, for Mr Bilham, to whom distance, both in space and time, had lent an almost fabulous enchantment. If only, I thought, it were Mr Bilham, instead of Alison, who was coming to stay! I wished, indeed, that it could have been Mr Bilham's family, instead of the Drake-Connollys, who were stricken with that mysterious 'Illness'—though this, as I realized, wouldn't really have helped matters much, since Mr Bilham, even if his household had been stricken by the Black Death itself, would most certainly not have been invited to spend a summer holiday with us at Sandgate.

23

I was, in fact, in anything but a favourable mood for the reception of Alison; and the knowledge that I was expected to be more than usually kind and well-behaved did nothing to make her arrival more welcome. On the day when she did, in fact, arrive, it happened that my state of mind was even less receptive than usual; for, that very afternoon, I had made what seemed to me to be a botanical discovery of the first importance—I had found, for the first time, a plant of henbane; it grew on the grassy slope by the side of the funicular lift at Sandgate, above the road which we still called the 'New Cutting' (though in fact it wasn't any longer new). The henbane, with its creamy, purple-veined flowers and clammy leaves, seemed to me an immensely exciting *trouvaille*; I knew it to be 'deadly poison', and could well imagine it as being a suitable ingredient of the witches' cauldron in *Macbeth*.

We returned to the house, on this red-letter afternoon, to find that Alison had already arrived. She was much the same as I remembered her, though she seemed to have become, in the last few months, considerably older and more 'leggy', and appeared to be rather alarmingly self-possessed. At the same time, she struck me as being a great deal more ordinary than I had supposed—no doubt for the very good reason that I was no longer in love with her, but also, perhaps, because I was now seeing her for the first time in ordinary surroundings, deprived of the romantic and alien background of School with which I had up till now associated her. She was, in fact, just a little girl, like other little girls; I thought, nostalgically, of Mr Bilham driving his pony-cart so dashingly through the lanes of the Elham Valley; then, remembering my promise to be kind and considerate to the newcomer, I held out to Alison, for her inspection, my newly-gathered bunch of henbane.

She sniffed at it (rather patronizingly, I thought) and immediately wrinkled up her nose in disgust.

'Pff—' she exclaimed, burying her face in a handkerchief, 'what a *filthy* stink!'

I was outraged by such disrespectful treatment of my exciting 'find', and assured her that henbane was 'very rare'— a statement which, alas, was not true, though at that moment, I am sure (having never myself found the plant before), I genuinely believed it.

'I don't care how rare it is,' Alison retorted, 'all I know is, it stinks like a polecat.'

It was a bad beginning; but worse—far worse—was to follow. The next morning I was encouraged to 'show Alison the garden'. Very cool and self-possessed, she accompanied me down the steps.

'Haven't you any greenhouses?' she asked, and, when I admitted that we had none, informed me that *her* family had lots, simply acres of them, full of peaches, figs and nectarines. Rather injudiciously, I proffered the Bushes as an alternative attraction: Alison looked critically at my 'places', and said that she supposed I had been trying to make a garden. I wisely remained silent; and Alison, with an air of ineffable boredom, established herself in the crook of the tamarisk bough where, in the past, I had spent so many hours in composing *vers libres* in her honour.

Today, I could only crouch, humiliatingly, beneath her swinging feet. Despite the fear and hostility with which she inspired me, I couldn't quite forget that this was, after all, the authentic, flesh-and-blood Alison with whom—before the advent of Mr Bilham—I had been so desperately in love. Hating her, I was nevertheless her slave; and when, later, she suggested that we should play 'Bluebeard', I was perfectly content to assume the rather ungrateful rôle of Sister Anne, while Alison, perched on the swaying bough, gazed out to sea with an expression of rapt expectation on her face, and intoned, in a kind of bardic phrenzy: 'Sister Anne, Sister Anne, do you see anybody coming?' To which I would reply, in a nervous and expressionless gabble: 'I see nothing but the sun which makes a dust and the grass which looks green.'

This game kept Alison happily occupied for quite a long time. Presently she broke off to inform me that, when she grew up, she intended to be an actress. Naturally I was immensely impressed by this piece of news; I had long ago come to the conclusion that actresses, besides having a very low standard of morality, were much the same as gipsies, and that they were in the habit of touring the country in gaily painted caravans such as I had once seen when I had been taken to Lord George Sanger's circus at Canterbury. That Alison should choose such a career seemed to me both exciting and slightly shocking. Would she, I asked anxiously, act in *revue* (for this form of entertainment, I had gathered, was particularly immoral)? Alison wasn't sure: she thought she probably might, but would prefer, on the whole, to take Shakespearean parts.

The morning dragged on: by lunch-time I was yawning and tremulous from sheer exhaustion. Alison, I realized, was altogether too grown-up and sophisticated for any real comradeship to be possible between us. In the afternoon, she expressed a desire to go down to the beach, and I was told to accompany her; fortunately the weather was sunless and chilly, and nobody suggested bathing. Alison amused herself by collecting shells and small pieces of feathery seaweed, while I sat disconsolately upon a damp rock, listening respectfully and somewhat nervously to such remarks as she condescended to let fall. Her sole topic of conversation appeared to be her family, of which she was very proud: she had been born in India, so she told me, and had had an Ayah—a fact by which, in spite of myself, I couldn't help being vastly impressed. Her father, I gathered, was something very grand indeed, and was known to his subordinates as the Burra Sahib; I imagined him, I think, as a real Indian, a kind of Arabian Nights figure in a turban, mounted upon a richly caparisoned elephant. Alison's mother, on the other hand, I presumed to be English, since her family lived at Hythe, and she had been presented, when a girl, to the King and Queen at Buckingham Palace.

I was impressed, it is true, by the evident grandeur of Alison's background; yet, as I listened to her rhapsodies, I became more and more bored and irritable, and found it increasingly difficult to respond with the respectful interest which she seemed to demand.

'I think my people are much nicer than yours,' she remarked suddenly. 'I expect it's because they have more money.'

This statement, though plausible enough, perhaps, as a mere proposition in social psychology, had the effect of provoking me into a passionate outburst of filial loyalty.

'I wouldn't have your old family,' I assured her, 'not on the end of a barge-pole.'

It wasn't a very brilliant riposte, but, so far as Alison was concerned, it proved remarkably—indeed alarmingly— effective.

'Oh *wouldn't* you,' she exclaimed, turning upon me in a sudden outburst of fury. 'Then let me tell you, you're the horridest little boy I've ever met in my whole life. My brother Nigel—who's younger than you—could jolly well lick you into a cocked hat, and my father, who's practically a king in India, could have you thrown to the crocodiles in the Ganges, just by lifting his finger—so you'd better look out for yourself, you beastly little devil.'

'That's a bad word,' I retorted, priggishly seizing my advantage.

'I know it is,' Alison shouted, with a jubilant shamelessness, 'I know it is—and that's why I called you it. You're a beastly little devil, d'you hear, a beastly little devil!' And she began to dance up and down before me, chanting in shrill, triumphant tones: 'Beastly little de-vil, beastly little de-vil!'

Miserable and utterly defenceless, upon my rock, I would willingly, at that moment, have killed her. It seemed impossible that this could really be the Alison Vyse who had played Puck so gracefully and so movingly, and whom I had once so desperately loved.

'Beastly little de-vil, beastly little de-vil'—the comminatory chant continued. At last, provoked past bearing, I decided that the moment had come to burn, finally, my boats.

'All right, then,' I interjected, 'if I'm a devil you're a ——, so there.'

The moment I had uttered the awful, the unforgivable word, I regretted it. I had only recently learnt of its existence: my brother had had a whole week's pocket-money stopped for using it to a visitor—a harmless old lady named Miss Featherstonehaugh. I looked at Alison in terror, half-hoping she hadn't heard: but alas, she had heard only too distinctly. I saw her recoil, with a histrionic gesture of horror: then, leaning forward, white-faced and eyes ablaze, she raised her hand and slapped me sharply across the face.

'That's a *filthy* word,' she spat at me, 'it's absolutely the filthiest, dreadfullest and wickedest word in the whole world.'

Unbearably humiliated, I stood up and faced her, burning at last with an anger as passionate as her own.

'I know it is,' I spat back at her, struck by the exquisite, the undeniable logic of my retort, 'I know it is—and that's why I called you it.'

Then, overwhelmed by pain and humiliation, I dissolved into a noisy and uncontrollable fit of weeping.

'It's no good blubbing,' pursued Alison mercilessly, 'you're a beastly, wicked, *vulgar* little boy, and I'm jolly well going to tell your people what you called me, so there.'

At this moment, perhaps fortunately, Ninnie appeared to announce that tea was ready. Alison, with her head in the air, refused to give any explanation of the distressing scene which, only too obviously, had just taken place. Later, however, when pressed, she admitted that I had used a 'very bad word', though she firmly refused to sully her own lips by repeating it.

'Is this true?' asked my mother. I hadn't the courage to deny it; but I refused, as firmly as Alison, to admit the full extent of my infamy.

I was promptly sent to bed in disgrace; and then ensued one of those endless, exhausting catechisms which I dreaded, at that time, more than anything else in the world. *Which* word had I used? Did it begin with a D? Did it begin—surely it couldn't have begun—with a B? Throughout that evening the dreadful inquisition proceeded; finally, by dint of excluding every letter of the alphabet in turn, the appalling syllables were extracted from me. I was left alone at last: but not to sleep. Far from being granted the absolution which, after such a confession, I might have expected, I realized that I was in worse disgrace than ever; and, as I tossed and turned beneath the sheets, I thought of that yellow-haired *Doppelgänger* that I had left to rot away, during the previous autumn, in the Bushes; and felt an obscure conviction that my present misery must be a kind of punishment for my disloyalty to that exquisite and epicene creature to whom, on that evening at Gaudeamus so long ago, I had made the gift of my heart.

For the next few days I remained in deep disgrace; yet this period of purgatory, however painful in itself, had its advantages, for I was at least kept, so far as possible, away from Alison: doubtless for fear that I should corrupt her morals still further and—possibly a more cogent reason—that she would report the fact to her 'people' on her return home.

At meal-times and on other occasions when we were unavoidably thrown together, Alison assumed an air of aloof disdain which I found infinitely more wounding than any overt hostility. For over a week I suffered from a violent and consuming misery such as I had never experienced before; at last, however, I learnt that Alison was to return to her grand-parents—whose household was now out of quarantine—on the day after tomorrow.

The prospect of an immediate release from my misery worked wonders; I began to feel that life, after all, might still hold some future pleasures in store. Oddly enough, Alison herself—doubtless because she, too, was about to escape from a situation which she plainly found intolerable—began sud-denly to make friendly overtures; to my astonishment, she even suggested that we went down to the Bushes. I could hardly refuse; and rather distrustfully—fearful lest her ami-cable gesture should prove a mere trap, designed to plunge me into some new and more awful disgrace—I trotted after her down the garden steps.

It was a grey, chilly August day with a hint of autumn in the air. The sea lapped sluggishly upon the shingle below; the first Michaelmas daisies already smouldered, with a melan-choly splendour, on the terrace below the quarter-deck. The whole occasion had for me a curious atmosphere of unreality: next term I was to go to school in Folkestone; it seemed to me that I was living, at the moment, in a kind of uncomfortable vacuum, suspended between the past and the future. By my side walked a little girl who, in her outward semblance, corresponded with somebody whom I had once passionately loved, but whom at the present moment I feared and detested. I wished I didn't hate her so much: almost, at this moment, I could feel my love for the original Alison, the light-footed nymph of *A Midsummer-night's Dream*, possess my heart again —a slender figure with plump cheeks and corn-coloured hair, wreathed about with the tufted, vernal inflorescence of that purple alyssum which in April hung its thick festoons from the rockery above the Bushes. Yet I knew that it wouldn't 'work': the real Alison, after all, was an intransigent and snobbish little girl, liable at any moment to pounce upon my innocent solecisms, and to 'put me in my place'. Moreover, I had committed the unforgivable sin—I had called her by the rudest name I knew, and thus forfeited all possible claim upon her respect or friendship. I was a leper, a pariah, scarcely fit to be walking by her side at all.

We pushed our way into the Bushes: I had not visited my 'places' for a week or more, and they were looking untidy and decrepit.

'You ought to tidy up your "garden",' said Alison, patronizingly.

'It's not a garden,' I replied, mechanically—and immediately wished I had kept silent.

'Oh, isn't it? Well, what is it, then?'

'It's a place,' I said sullenly, without conviction, and with a profound sense of my own futility.

'A *place*?' Alison echoed. 'But what *sort* of place?'

'It's not *any* sort of place—it's just a place,' I repeated, hopelessly.

'But it must be something—is it meant to be a garage?' Here Alison picked up a toy motor from beneath a screen of tamarisk sprigs.

'No, it's *not* a garage,' I protested, with rising anger.

'Well, you might tell me what it's meant to be—it must be something. A place can't just be a *place*,' Alison asserted, with a cold reasonableness which horrified me. I realized that what she said was, in fact, perfectly logical and accurate; yet I knew, also, without being able to express it, that my 'places' were unique and self-sufficient—they were *not* garages or forts or anything else; they were just Places, meaningless to others, perhaps, but to myself immensely and perennially significant.

'*My* places are just Places,' I insisted, obstinately.

Alison gave a mocking and rather affected little peal of laughter.

'How absurd you are,' she said, in an intolerably superior and grown-up voice. 'Of course, you can't *help* being only seven years old, but I do think you're an awful baby for your age. My brother Nigel's much more sensible than you are—he's got a real toy garage, with six motors in it.'

With this she wandered away, with a *dégagé* air, down the steps to the quarter-deck. I made no attempt to follow her; instead, I remained crouched beneath the tamarisk, surveying with a sad and disillusioned eye the terraces and escarpments which I had so lovingly excavated from the barren, sandy soil. I looked at the little caves and dug-outs, in which lurked the toy motors and the lead soldiers; there, too, were the remains of that larger cave in which the stuffed airman and, later, 'Alison' herself had been so cruelly imprisoned. . . . Suddenly

I was overcome by a black, destructive passion of hatred for my own creations; sobbing with an uninhibited violence, I began to kick, recklessly, at the little boarded-in platforms, the caves, the pallisades of twigs; in a few moments nothing remained of my famous 'place' but a desolate ruin, strewn with broken fragments of boxwood and with the prostrate bodies of the toy soldiers.

For several minutes I stood there, gazing mournfully at the wreckage; and in that moment it seemed to me that, with the destruction of all that I had held most dear, a part of myself, too, had disintegrated and fallen into ruin. Obscurely, I realized that I should never be quite the same again; something had happened which made the 'self' which I had thought of, up till now, as being uniquely and unmistakably my own, seem suddenly remote and alien, like somebody whom I had once known, but who had begun, already, to fade into the limbo of the past.

Aimlessly, aware of a desolate emptiness in my heart and mind, I wandered up the garden towards the house; in the bed beneath the tall privet hedge, the fuchsias hung like lurid eardrops in the ears of barbarous women; from the beach below, I could hear the high, incessant yapping of a small dog; and, more remotely, from somewhere far out in the mist-shrouded bay, came the long, melancholy booming of a foghorn.

Alison departed the next day; soon I had all but forgotten those disastrous ten days which she had spent with us. Yet I had, none the less, learnt something from my encounter with her: for I realized now—and I was never to forget it—that the people with whom I imagined myself 'in love' were in fact not real people at all, but mere fleshless phantoms, images of 'reality' reflected in the distorting mirror of my own imagination.

At Easter, we returned once more to our country cottage; and here a new disillusion awaited me: for Mr Bilham had insensibly changed in the interval—not only did he seem less disposed to be friendly, but he had ceased to wear riding breeches. He was, I noticed, beginning to grow rather fat; he smiled a good deal less; and he had grown a moustache of which I could not wholly approve. He had also, as I learned in due course, become engaged to be married, which no doubt went far to explain the deterioration in his character. A few months later, I heard that his marriage had duly taken place; shortly afterwards, he threw up his job with the baker, and moved to Herne Bay, where his wife's brother, it seemed, had very conveniently offered him a partnership in a motor business.

As for Alison, I never saw her again. Soon after her visit, I heard that the Drake-Connollys had left Hythe, and that Alison was to rejoin her parents in India, where, it seemed, the Burra Sahib had been appointed to a new job in a 'healthy' neighbourhood.

During the next few years my memories of the real, flesh-and-blood Alison became progressively more dim; I would hear of her now and again from friends of my sister who had known her at school; but as a person who lived and breathed and whom I might conceivably meet again she soon ceased to have any reality for me. Yet the Alison of my romantic phantasies—the little girl who had played Puck at Gaudeamus, and whom I had alternately petted (in the form of an ill-made rag doll) and punished by spells of solitary confinement in the Bushes—this Alison remained for me, in spite of everything, a kind of archetype of desirable girlhood, and years later, when

I had all but forgotten the circumstances of our real-life acquaintance, I would find myself thinking of her lithe, plump figure as I had seen it first upon the stage at Gaudeamus. Sometimes, too, when I happened to pay a visit to the Bushes, I would feel a faint stab of nostalgia, remembering those long summer afternoons when I had sat, mute and humiliated, beneath the tamarisk boughs, while Alison, enskied in their midst, had chanted her interminable runes. And once, many years later, when the overgrown thickets of periwinkle and mesembryanthemum were cut away from the base of the little slope, I came across a small, discoloured toy-soldier: sole survivor of that vanished race with whom, so many years before, I had peopled my closely-guarded and anonymous 'places'—those countries of the mind which lay, now, remote and unapproachable, beyond the Iron Curtain of puberty; countries to which, alas, no passport or visa could procure for me the right of entry, for I had long since forfeited my claim upon their hospitality.

Gerald Brockhurst

1

I T must have been during my first term at Oxford that I
became acquainted with Gerald Brockhurst; for I remember that our first meeting took place, over a pint of bitter,
in the 'Trout' at Godstow. During those first weeks as a
freshman, I had formed the habit of hiring a hack once or
twice a week and riding out to Port Meadow; I did this partly
because I liked it, and partly as an anti-social gesture—for, as
a conscientious (and even a militant) aesthete, I had naturally
refused to play any games. At the same time, I was not wholly
immune to the fetish of 'exercise'—a hangover, no doubt,
from my schooldays; and riding, though it might be anti-
social, was admitted (even by athletes) to be as good a way
as any other of shaking up one's liver.

Usually I rode in the afternoon: trotting cautiously—
'remote, unfriended, melancholy, slow'—through the outer
suburbs, cantering a few times round Port Meadow, and
returning, through the bleak November dusk, to tea and
crumpets in my rooms. Now and again, however, a fine
winter's morning would tempt me to cut lectures (I still went
to lectures at that time) and ride out before lunch; and it was
on one of these occasions that, having cantered dutifully, as
usual, round the meadows, I tethered my horse outside the
Trout and went into the bar for a drink. The keen, wintry

air, the exercise and, perhaps, an agreeable sense of playing truant, had induced in me a mood of unaccustomed heartiness: I felt positively doggish, and a match for any athlete. I ordered a pint of bitter—not because I particularly liked beer, but because it seemed the drink most suited to the occasion. I exchanged a few remarks—of a suitable heartiness, as I supposed—with the landlord; then, as my eyes strayed round the room, I observed another young man dressed, like myself, in riding-kit, standing at the opposite end of the bar. I had noticed, when I came in, that another horse was tethered nearby; and it was almost inevitable, in the circumstances, that my fellow-rider and I should fall into conversation.

He was a very ordinary-looking young man: not very tall, but heavily built and stocky, with broad shoulders and a thick, muscular neck. His face was round, blunt-featured and in no way distinguished, though the expression was pleasant enough; he wore a little toothbrush moustache, which was perhaps a recent acquisition, for he was inclined to pull at it, rather self-consciously, as he talked. No doubt it was partly the moustache which made him seem older than he was; certainly it didn't occur to me that he could be an undergraduate —I put him down vaguely, I think, as an Army officer in mufti, or possibly a gentleman farmer. His accent was 'educated' yet not obtrusively so: there was about it the faintest suggestion of some regional 'burr'. I was not, in any case, particularly interested in his background; I was content to accept him as just an ordinary, quite pleasant young man, who happened to share my taste for riding. In my present elated mood I should have enjoyed talking to almost anybody; and this chance acquaintance, with his bluff, bucolic appearance, seemed (like the beer) entirely suited to the occasion.

I haven't the faintest recollection of what we talked about, though I should imagine that our conversation was mainly restricted to horses, beer and the weather. What I do remember is that we drank several pints of bitter—more than I was accustomed to—and that when the time came to start back, I found it uncommonly difficult to climb into the saddle, and even more difficult, once I had managed to do so, to remain there. My new acquaintance, fortunately, was also riding back to Oxford (he had hired his horse, as it turned out, from the same stable), and we set out together along the tow-path; more than once my horse stumbled, and only my companion's strong arm saved me from disaster. Before we parted, we arranged to go out together on an afternoon later in the same week.

When the time came, I half hoped he wouldn't turn up, for I was inclined to mistrust such chance acquaintanceships, formed under the influence of alcohol; for one thing, I didn't want to become involved with a bore, and being, moreover, an indifferent rider, I was more than a little afraid of making a fool of myself. Gerald, however (I had discovered that his name was Gerald Brockhurst), arrived punctually at the stables, and we started out towards Port Meadow. My qualms, as I soon realized, had been unjustified: for Gerald showed no disposition to laugh at my awkwardness; nor did he seem in the least the sort of person with whom one was likely to become tediously 'involved'. As a companion, I found him tactful and unexacting, and, despite the somewhat narrow and conventional range of his interests, I didn't, as I had half expected, find him a bore.

I discovered that he was, after all, a member of the university, only a year or two older than myself, and that he was studying medicine. This I found mildly distressing, for medical students were regarded as a slightly inferior breed at Oxford in those days. Gerald, as though guessing what was in my mind, explained that he would have preferred to go to Cambridge, but that his father had insisted upon Oxford.

'I always wanted to be a doctor, right from the word go,' Gerald confided. 'But the pater was dead against it—he wanted me to go into the family business. We had quite a bust-up just before I left school; finally, I sort of compromised, and said I'd come up here.'

'I suppose your father was up himself?' I asked, mildly curious.

Gerald chuckled.

'Not on your life—he started in business when he was sixteen. He's one of these self-made blokes, you see—civil engineer up at Northampton. He's retired now—got a little place in Surrey. I suppose,' Gerald added, turning to me with a shy smile, 'I suppose he'd got a sort of idea that Oxford was a bit more posh than the other place—you know, the kind of thing you see in the papers, gilded young aristocrats and all that.'

I realized, now, why Gerald hadn't seemed like an under-graduate: it wasn't only the moustache, or even the hint of a provincial accent, but something more deeply rooted—a kind of precocious maturity, an ability to get to grips with life, inherited from his father, and from the class from which his father had sprung. I began to suspect that Gerald was by no means so 'ordinary' as I had at first supposed; and his adult, realistic attitude, combined with his physical toughness and confidence, made me feel curiously unfledged and ineffectual.

He didn't say much more about himself that day, or, indeed, on the days which followed. For the rest of that term we rode together fairly regularly, and in a quiet, non-committal way we became very friendly; yet oddly enough it was never suggested, by either of us, that we should meet elsewhere. It didn't occur to me, for instance, to ask Gerald back to tea in college; nor did Gerald invite me to his rooms (which, I gathered, were somewhere out towards Iffley). If Gerald had other friends, he didn't talk about them; and I suspect that there was a tacit understanding between us that we belonged to different and perhaps mutually uncongenial 'sets'. In my own case, as it happened, this feeling was in no way justified, for I didn't—apart from one or two acquaintances in my own college—belong to any set at all. I was, in fact, extremely lonely during that first term, and should have been glad enough of Gerald's company at other times; yet our friendship remained limited to our afternoon rides, or an occasional morning jaunt when we would finish up, convivially, at the Trout, with a meal of bread-and-cheese and beer.

By the end of the term, Gerald had become, in a dim and unobtrusive way, a part of my life: I didn't think of him as a 'friend', but merely as someone quite pleasant whom I happened to see rather a lot of; rather like one's wine-merchant, or the head-waiter at a favourite restaurant—people with whom one was on the most amicable terms, yet never met elsewhere than in the particular ambience to which they belonged. In the case of Gerald, this ambience was the grey, frost-bound meadows beyond Godstow, the tow-path, and the bar at the Trout; to this day, when I think of him, it is against such a background that I imagine his squat, stocky figure, his rather podgy face, and his attractive, mildly ironic grin. I think of him as he was then—twenty or twenty-one, I suppose, yet giving an impression of being a good deal older; and indeed, Gerald was one of those people who, maturing early, alter very little between youth and middle-age. Of some men one can say that they belong, by nature, to a characteristic, a 'typical' age-group: Gerald I should place at round about thirty; he changed remarkably little during the time I knew him, and if he seemed, when we first met, to be far older and more mature than myself, it was, oddly enough, his air of youth and *naïveté* which was to strike me most forcibly at our last encounter, nearly twenty years later.

Meanwhile—during these first weeks of our acquaintance —he remained for me a vague, almost impersonal presence: our association was primarily physical, a communion of bodily activity; and if I thought of Gerald at all, when I wasn't actually with him, it was his body that I chiefly remembered —the broad shoulders, the muscular neck, the cropped darkish hair. I hadn't, as yet, invested him with a 'personality': he remained, so to speak, on the wrong side of the counter— somebody with whom one passed the time of day and discussed the weather, but who ceased to exist, for all practical purposes, once one was out of the shop.

By the end of term, however, Gerald did begin to impinge upon me as a personality in his own right. Certain people seem never to become quite 'real' until one has observed them afresh through the eyes of a third person: viewed thus, from an unaccustomed angle, they acquire, so to speak, an added dimension, one sees them for the first time 'in the round', like a familiar photograph seen through a stereoscope. Gerald, I suppose, was such a person; up till now, he had remained for me, as it were, two-dimensional, like a 'flat' character in a novel; and, but for an accidental encounter with another of my friends, he might well, so far as I was concerned, have continued in the colourless and undistinguished rôle for which, with some injustice, I had originally cast him.

One afternoon after riding, as we were walking out of the

stables in Walton Street, we ran straight into Eric Anquetil, with whom I had lately struck up a friendship. Seeing us, he hailed me across the street, and I was obliged to introduce him to Gerald. The situation was fraught, for me, with an absurdly disproportionate embarrassment: if Gerald had been one of the town prostitutes I couldn't have felt more self-conscious. I had not mentioned him to Eric—or, at most, had referred to him evasively as 'someone I went riding with'; nor, for that matter, had I mentioned Eric to Gerald. No two people, I felt, could have been more ill-assorted: Eric, on this occasion, was looking more than usually aesthetic, in a pale-grey suit, shantung tie and suède shoes; Gerald, I felt sure, would be embarrassed and perhaps morally outraged; and Eric, no doubt, would think Gerald impossibly dim and bourgeois.

As it happened, I couldn't have been more mistaken: expecting the worst, I was agreeably surprised to find that my two friends appeared, after a couple of minutes, to be on the best of terms. Soon they were chattering away nineteen to the dozen—about the latest film at the Super Cinema, about Fred Astaire, about the barmaids at the Clarendon: subjects which it would never have occurred to me to broach, and about which, in any case, I was profoundly ignorant. Eric, with a social aplomb which I could only helplessly envy, contrived to strike just the right note of heartiness combined with a touch of aristocratic *dandysme*; as for Gerald, I had never heard him so loquacious, and his manner had a vivacity and charm of which I had never supposed him capable. To be frank, I felt ever so slightly jealous: Gerald, after all, was *my* discovery; yet it had remained for Eric—improbably enough —to reveal his true 'personality', to put him, as they say nowadays, 'in the picture'.

Encouraged by the success of this encounter, I asked Gerald

back to tea in my rooms. We gossiped amicably about trivialities over our crumpets and anchovy-toast; Gerald looked at my books, we played the gramophone (rather surprisingly, as I thought, Gerald was fond of music, with a special liking for Beethoven). Relaxed and euphoric after riding, I began to feel a new and more positive pleasure in his company; Gerald, I thought, if not particularly stimulating or glamorous, was an extremely pleasant and 'comfortable' person to be with.

As for Eric, he seemed to have taken an instant liking to Gerald, as I discovered that same evening when we met in Hall.

'I don't know why you've been keeping him under a bushel for so long,' he complained. 'I think he's very nice: I do so like that *sort* of athlete—so restful, don't you think? And it's odd and pleasing that his name should be Gerald.'

'Why odd—*or* pleasing?' I enquired with bewilderment.

'Oh, haven't you noticed? In novels, people like that are *always* called Gerald. There's one in E. M. Forster, and another in Lawrence—you know, the man in *Women in Love*—and I once read a novel by Gilbert Frankau, when I was at school, called *Gerald Cranston's Lady*; the hero was just the same type, terrifically hearty and military, with a moustache.'

'You ought to write a little monograph on the subject,' I suggested.

'Yes, I did think of it—or we might start some very queer, esoteric sort of society, and make Gerald Brockhurst the president.'

Thereafter, for some considerable time, Eric and I 'collected' Geralds; it was odd how often they seemed to support Eric's theory. Once we even went so far as to invite a totally unknown undergraduate to tea, merely on the strength of his Christian name (he had, I think, written a letter to the *Isis*).

What pretext we invented for the invitation, I cannot remember; but the young man duly turned up (he was at Keble) and proved to be a person of singularly revolting aspect, with rimless glasses and false teeth.

'So much for your theory,' I said to Eric, when we had at last got rid of him.

'Not a bit of it,' Eric retorted, firmly, 'he was merely the exception which proves the rule.'

I rode once more with Gerald that term, and afterwards Eric invited us both to tea in his rooms. I was still a little nervous about Gerald's possible reactions to Eric (and vice versa); I need not have worried, for Eric had plainly laid himself out to be charming, and Gerald—as I was now beginning to realize—possessed a social flair which, though it differed in kind from Eric's more sophisticated code of manners, was not less adequate, and could indeed, on occasion, prove a good deal more effective.

There was something admirably solid and 'rooted' about Gerald: sitting back, lazily yet with an air of calm alertness, in his armchair, he seemed entirely at his ease; he spoke little, yet such remarks as he made were, if not brilliant, at least sensible and to the point. Our conversation was, to say the least, uninhibited: Eric, it was evident, had decided that Gerald was 'steeped' ('steeped in the highest philosophy')—or, if not positively steeped, at least faintly tinged with the appropriate greenery-yallery pigment. Once or twice I feared that Gerald, despite his apparent 'unshockableness', might jib at some of Eric's more outrageous remarks; yet he didn't, to my extreme relief, seem in the least perturbed. At the most he would raise his brows and give a slight shrug; then his face would relax again into a broad, tolerant grin—as though (it occurred to me) he were watching the undignified antics of a couple of naughty children. Once again, as when I had first met him, I was struck by his air of maturity; and I had an uneasy feeling that Eric and I were not, after all, quite so adult and sophisticated as we liked to suppose.

Gerald, as it happened, was quite a good Latin scholar, and was perfectly capable, in this respect, of meeting Eric upon his own ground: a fact by which (as I observed with a slight, ignoble relish) Eric was ever so slightly piqued. Gerald, moreover, rather surprisingly—or so it seemed to us—had read *Antic Hay* and even *Ulysses*.

'Of course,' he remarked of the latter, 'I enjoyed the dirty bits, just like anyone else; but if you want my honest opinion, I found it a bloody dull book'—a judgment which (though I wouldn't have openly admitted it) delighted me, for it coincided precisely with my own private opinion.

When Gerald left, I accompanied him as far as the porter's lodge. As we emerged into the street, Gerald paused, regarding me ruminatively; then said suddenly:

'What about coming to tea with *me*, sometime?'

For some reason the invitation startled me: somehow it had become a habit to think of Gerald as a guest rather than as a host; and it came as a slight shock to realize that Gerald, after all, had his own background—his rooms in the Iffley Road, his work and (presumably) those other friends whom he never referred to, but who must nevertheless exist.

'Make it tomorrow,' Gerald went on, before I could reply. 'We could have a high-tea—my landlady's rather good at that sort of thing—and then go out on the booze somewhere.'

It would be hard to say just why I refused Gerald's invitation; but refuse it I did. Tomorrow was the last day of term, and perhaps, with some idea of celebration in my mind, I was unwilling to tie myself to a definite engagement. I liked Gerald very much, but I didn't, as yet, regard him as an intimate—or even as a particularly valued—friend, and I wasn't prepared to run the risk of being saddled with a bore. At this period, moreover, I liked to imagine myself against a particular social background—a largely imaginary world of cocktails, smart people and witty conversation—and high-tea with a rather dim medical student in the Iffley Road didn't, I felt, quite fit into the picture. Nor did the prospect of subsequently 'going on the booze' seem specially attractive, for I hadn't at that time developed a taste for alcohol, except in the rarefied atmosphere of 'aesthetic' cocktail-parties, and Gerald, I had every reason to suppose, was almost exclusively a beer-drinker, with a preference for what, in those days, I would have snobbishly stigmatized as 'low pubs'.

I fabricated some vague excuse—a quite fictitious dinner-party—and I knew at once that Gerald wasn't taken in.

'Oh, come off it,' he said, with a disbelieving grin. 'Put 'em off—tell 'em you're going to your grandmother's funeral—you'd have much more fun on a pub-crawl. There's a decent little house I know in St Ebbe's—it's not often progged, and the beer's bloody good.'

For two pins I would have changed my mind; in my heart I knew that Gerald was right—I should have enjoyed a night-out with him far more than an evening spent among my acknowledged 'friends'. Perversely, however, I stuck to my guns, and insisted that my imaginary dinner-party was an important occasion, and that my host would be mortally offended if I didn't turn up.

I saw Gerald's face fall, and knew that he was offended. Once again, I almost changed my mind; but I had left it too late.

'Oh well, if you won't, you won't,' Gerald said abruptly, his voice taking on a faint, unaccustomed edge of impatience. Then, suddenly, he grinned at me broadly and held out his hand.

'Well, so long,' he exclaimed cheerfully, 'see you next term.'

He grasped my hand with a painful violence, and turned away. The sudden gesture had taken me aback—partly, I daresay, because it wasn't 'done' to shake hands at Oxford in those days. I watched him walk away across Beaumont Street; as he reached the pavement, he turned and smiled again, raising his arm in a gesture of farewell.

'Hope you enjoy your dinner-party,' he shouted.

I waved back, rather feebly; then returned, guilty and disconsolate, to my rooms, where I sported my oak and tried, with a conspicuous lack of success, to read *The Brothers Karamazoff*. Later, after a penitential dinner in Hall, I wandered out by myself into the town: along the Cornmarket and down the High as far as Magdalen Bridge. It was a mild, damp evening; the lights gleamed feebly on the wet pavements, and a faint wind blew the rain against my face. A mood of romantic, Byronic melancholy descended upon me: leaning over the bridge, I was suddenly aware of the intolerable ache of loneliness—a sensation which had afflicted me, intermittently, for as long as I could remember, but which seemed, on this rainy autumnal night, more acute than ever before. I longed for friendship, yet I realized, with a gloomy clairvoyance, that I should almost certainly never achieve it. Too timid and repressed, myself, to make the first move, it seemed that I was ineluctably compelled, by some perverse instinct, to reject the kindly advances of others. Once, when I was six years old, I had longed above all things to become the friend of a little boy who was our neighbour; nothing, as it happened, could have been easier to arrange; yet when an opportunity occurred to go to a children's party at which he was to be present, I became terrified, and obstinately refused to go. It was just the same with my adult relations: no sooner did somebody I liked proffer me the hand of friendship, than I winced away as though at some threat of violence—horrified of committing myself, of 'giving myself away', and fatally mistrustful of my capacity to reciprocate, with genuine affection, the feelings of another.

Gerald Brockhurst, as I had come to realize during the last few weeks, was a thoroughly nice person, with whom I should have liked to be friends; moreover, he showed unmistakable signs of wanting to be friends with me—a fact which, in situations of this kind, never failed to surprise me. Yet I had recoiled, as usual, from his friendly approaches— and, which was worse, had recoiled so blatantly and with so little tact, that he had been quite justifiably offended, and in all probability would not renew his overtures. I cursed myself for my rudeness and—even more vehemently—for my snobbery and self-deceit. Gerald, I had told myself, was 'dim', a nobody, a potential bore; but I knew, in my heart, that he was nothing of the kind.

2

Surprisingly enough, I didn't see Gerald again till nearly halfway through the following term. During this comparatively short space of time, I had contrived almost to forget his existence; or at most I remembered him merely as a dim companion of my freshman days, whom I should in all probability never run across again. I suspect, in fact, that in thus banishing Gerald from my mind, I was trying to by-pass, as it were, my own feelings of guilt about him. At our last meeting, I had been tactless if not downright offensive; but there was, I think, another, more important reason for thus conveniently 'forgetting' him.

At this period of my life I was much troubled by the thought that I was 'escaping' from something which I was wont to refer to, with a portentous vagueness, as 'reality'; I was aware, in a dim and inchoate way, that my life was lived largely in terms of phantasy; somewhere, at the back of my mind, I envisaged a contrasted mode of existence which was not only more 'real' than my present one, but infinitely more desirable. This vision of the Good Life remained, it is true, exceedingly ill-defined; but it certainly included, among other essential requirements, a friendship with some nice, solid (and preferably 'unintellectual') person, a kind of elder brother to whom I could confide all my troubles, and who could be relied upon to share the burden of my own so difficult and delicately-adjusted temperament. I had already encountered one or two possible candidates for this singularly thankless rôle; so far, however, my attempts to enlist their sympathies had proved notably unsuccessful, and I had been forced, once again, to retire ignominiously into the cosy if somewhat depressing bolt-hole of my phantasy-life. In Gerald, I suppose, I had recognized yet another of these potential Big Brothers; but by this time I had developed a chronic fear of being humiliated: once bitten, twice shy—I wouldn't be 'had' again.

During these first few weeks of the Lent term, I had almost given up riding: partly because of the weather (which was particularly severe), and partly owing to one of those sudden and largely irrational fits of parsimony which are only possible to incorrigible spendthrifts like myself. Moreover, I had made a number of new acquaintances, with whom, as often as not,

I would spend the afternoons listening to gramophone records at Acott's, followed by tea at the Cadena or the Super.

Yet the memory of Gerald did faintly persist, and once or twice, with a lingering sense of guilt, I almost decided to seek him out; other activities, however, intervened; and the fact that Gerald himself had made no sign seemed to indicate that he had no very urgent desire to renew the acquaintance.

One day, however, when I returned to college after a night in London, I was told by the porter that a gentleman had been asking for me—a Mr Brockhurst. Had he left any message? He had not. My sense of guilt began, once again, to assert itself: I really would go and look up Gerald—this very day; but then I remembered that I had promised to go to tea with a man at Oriel, and afterwards to a dance on Boar's Hill. For several days, indeed, I was kept busy with engagements of one sort or another, and soon the idea of Gerald had begun to recede, once again, into the background of my consciousness.

And then, one afternoon, I ran full-tilt into him in the Broad, outside Blackwell's. Overcome by a sudden and violent embarrassment, I blushed scarlet. Gerald, however, appeared perfectly self-possessed, and greeted me with his usual bluff bonhomie; from his manner one might have supposed that we had been seeing one another every day for the last two months.

'Where have you been hiding yourself?' he demanded. 'I came and looked you up last week, as a matter of fact, but you'd gone to Town.'

I muttered something about having been very busy—adding (with dubious relevance) that the weather had been too bad for riding. It was a feeble effort on my part, and I could see that Gerald didn't even pretend to take it seriously. I had half turned away, to hide my blushes, and was gazing, with a wholly assumed interest, at a new variorum edition of Keats in Blackwell's window; when I turned round again, it was to find Gerald's eyes fixed upon me with an expression of mildly contemptuous amusement. Suddenly his face broke into the broad, amiable grin which I remembered.

'Oh well, let's go and have some tea,' he suggested, with brusque geniality.

I could hardly refuse, and followed him, obediently, down the Broad towards the Cornmarket. I was still hot with embarrassment, and would have escaped if I could; yet I knew in my heart that I was genuinely glad to have met him again.

We went to the Moorish Tea-rooms, a gloomy and self-consciously arty establishment much frequented by visiting parents of undergraduates. Over our tea and scones we spoke vapidly of current topics; my embarrassment persisted, and I felt shy and tongue-tied, as though I were a school-boy being taken out to tea by his housemaster. Nor were our surroundings calculated to increase my self-possession: the room was small and cramped, and the few other customers —mostly old ladies—spoke in sibilant undertones, as though they were in church. Gerald, perhaps realizing how I was feeling, chattered on about his college rugger-team, the weather, a 'bloody good show' (*Hit the Deck*) which he had taken his sister to in the vac. . . . Looking at him, I felt, with an inward detachment, what a remarkably nice person he really was: beneath the carapace of heartiness, the callow Wodehousian pose, he possessed, I thought, a kind of natural distinction—a quality which combined an innate sensitiveness with a knotty, unyielding strength. Tough as he was, there was nothing in the least oafish about him; above all (I thought) he gave an impression of cohesion, of being, more than most people, 'all-of-a-piece'. I was struck, once again, by his air of maturity: perhaps his clothes contributed to this effect—the old tweed coat with leather patches on the elbows, the plain, well-fitting shirt and school tie; I was reminded, suddenly, of my own elder brother, and for a moment my old, warm feeling for Gerald revived. I knew, as he sat placidly talking over his tea, that he was prepared to let bygones be bygones, and accept me as a friend; yet I knew, too, that I couldn't with any honesty accept his unspoken offer. I realized that I had left things too late: I was committed (or so it seemed) to a world and a way of life in which Gerald could have no part.

Tongue-tied, miserable, acutely aware of my own inadequacy, I longed to escape, to slink away into the dim, squalid phantasy-world which was (as I was beginning to realize) my natural habitat. *Non sum dignus*, I thought, with a mournful acquiescence; and, hardly aware of what Gerald was saying, allowed my eyes to stray across the room to a table in the centre, somewhat isolated from the rest, at which sat a very young man, obviously a freshman like myself, with a middle-aged woman whom I guessed to be his mother. They were quite evidently having one of those 'little talks' which are so liable to occur towards the end of one's first term at the university: the young man looked very unhappy—he was a colourless person, dressed unsuitably in silver-grey Oxford 'bags' and a crimson shantung tie. Plainly he was not enjoying his tea in the very least. Suddenly I heard his voice rise, in a plaintive falsetto, above the muted chatter of the old ladies.

'But don't you see, Mummy,' he wailed, nearly in tears, and raising both hands in an agonized though ineffectual gesture, 'don't you see, Life is so frightfully *difficult*.'

I looked at Gerald; he looked at me; and simultaneously, stricken by a sudden and quite uncontrollable hysteria, we burst out laughing. It was appalling, it was unpardonable:

we stifled our laughter in our handkerchiefs, pretended to be coughing, tried with an increasing agony to control ourselves. . . . It was useless: finally we bolted, incontinently, for the door; I suppose we paid our bill; all I can remember is that we managed to stumble down the stairs, still hooting and guffawing uncontrollably, into the street. On the pavement, we met each other's eyes, and our laughter was redoubled.

'Oh Mummy,' squeaked Gerald, in a wholly unsuccessful attempt at a 'nancy-boy' falsetto, 'Oh Mummy, Life is so frightfully *difficult*.'

An improbable *deus ex machina*, the poor, vapid undergraduate had succeeded, all unwittingly, in breaking the ice: suddenly the constraint of the past two months had vanished, Gerald and I were reunited, as though by magic, in the old, easy comradeship. Still laughing, we turned into the Cornmarket; by now our laughter had ceased to have any relation to its original cause—we laughed, quite simply, because we couldn't stop.

'Come on,' Gerald managed to mutter at last, through his giggles, 'let's go and have a drink at the Clarry—I'll go clean off my rocker if I don't get a pint inside me.'

I followed Gerald, without protest, into the bar of the Clarendon Hotel; nor did I raise any objection when he ordered two pints of bitter.

The Clarendon bar, in those days, had a somewhat dubious reputation: it was proggable (though the hotel lounge was not), and the undergraduates who, at their peril, frequented it, tended to be hearty, horsey and rather truculently heterosexual. This latter proclivity was admirably catered for by the barmaids, who were personable young women, and reputed to be of easy virtue. One of them was a tall, buxom brunette called Gladys: she must have been at least thirty-five, perhaps more, and (as I had heard Eric say) was doubtless a useful dumping-ground for a refractory Oedipus complex. The other, Kathleen, was younger, and affected a roguish, come-hither air borrowed, one would have guessed, from Miss Clara Bow. I had only once visited the bar before, and its atmosphere of raffish heartiness would have alarmed me if I had been with anybody but Gerald. I recognized one or two people I knew by sight: sporting types in loud checks, with very short hair and a pronounced tendency to acne; one associated them inevitably with high-powered sports-cars and week-ends at Maidenhead.

'Not a bad spot, this,' Gerald remarked, swallowing half his pint at a draught. 'And the beer's not bad. Come on, drink up—you're sipping it as if it was vintage port.'

With some difficulty I swallowed the rest of my pint.

'It's my turn, anyway,' I said, and ordered two more.

'This is the life,' Gerald said, with a satisfied sigh. 'You know,' he added suddenly, after a longish pause, and eyeing me quizzically across the table, 'you know, the trouble with *you* is you don't get around enough.'

'Get around?' I queried, feeling rather bewildered.

'Well, you know what I mean—getting around, seeing people, enjoying yourself.'

'But I *do* get around,' I protested, rather tartly. 'And I know any amount of people—more than you do, probably.'

'Oh well, yes—*those* sort of people—' Gerald retorted with a flicker of impatience, then checked himself, looking mildly embarrassed. 'What I mean is,' he continued, awkwardly, 'the people you know are all the same sort of type—awfully brainy and highbrow and all that, but they must be a bit of a strain, aren't they? Mind you,' he added, hastily, 'old Eric's all right—how is he by the way?—but most of the blokes I've seen you around with look a bit sissyfied, if you don't mind my saying so.'

With anybody but Gerald I should have lost my temper. I was extremely angry, but something in Gerald's face made me swallow down the cutting retort which rose to my lips.

'I didn't know you *had* seen me around,' I replied at last, with what I hoped was a just perceptible irony.

'Oh, I've caught sight of you once or twice, you know,' said Gerald casually. 'No, what I mean is—' he paused again, screwing up his face into a comical frown—'what I mean is, you want taking out of yourself, if you see what I mean.'

I managed a rather sickly smile.

'I see,' I said. 'And do you propose to perform this interesting operation yourself?'

Gerald grinned.

'I wouldn't mind having a stab at it,' he said. 'No, what I mean is, you don't seem to know any ordinary sort of blokes —the sort of chap you can barge around and have a good time with, without all this highbrow talk.'

'I know *you*,' I retorted, stung at last into irritability.

Gerald gave a mocking smile.

'Yes, but you're not quite sure whether you want to or not, are you?'

I felt my face turn as red as a beetroot. That Gerald should thus suddenly decide to burn his boats—or, to be perfectly accurate, *my* boats—was the very last thing I had expected. I was profoundly shocked, and could only stare at him speechlessly. Gerald, for his part, looked perfectly composed, and continued to gaze at me calmly, his lips still parted in a half-smile.

'What *utter* nonsense,' I burst out at last. 'Why, I—I mean, you know perfectly well—' I broke off, knowing that it was worse than useless to defend myself: what Gerald had said was no more than the truth, and nothing I could say would convince him to the contrary.

'All right, all right, keep your hair on,' Gerald said hastily. 'Drink up, and I'll get the other half.'

Barely conscious of what I was doing, I emptied my glass. I felt outraged, unbearably humiliated: it was as though I had been stripped naked, and subjected to some shameful physical assault. Yet oddly enough I didn't feel any anger towards Gerald personally; I knew that my humiliation, however painful, was deserved; and I even began to feel, at the back of my mind, a curious sense of relief. My relationship with Gerald had, as I realized, been based on a lie; now the cat was out of the bag, and it was time to 'have things out'.

Soon Gerald came back with our refilled glasses.

'Bung-ho!' he exclaimed, with so exactly the air of a 'Sapper' hero that I had to laugh. He took a gulp of beer, then leaned over the table towards me. 'Sorry if I was a bit crude in my methods,' he said, 'but I'm no good at beating about the bush.'

With an effort, I met his clear, candid gaze, and felt suddenly more at ease.

'The fact is,' he went on, in halting tones, yet with a certain air of decision, 'the fact is, I think you're a pretty decent kind of bloke—I sort of took to you from the first, if you see what I mean, and I thought we were going to be pals, but of course—' Gerald paused, lowered his eyes, then looked up again with a shy and rather charming smile—'of course, I realize you're quite a different type from me, and you probably find me a crashing bore and all that—'

'But I don't—'

'Shut up and let me finish,' Gerald cut in, with a sudden, half-comic violence. 'I know I'm not clever and artistic like all those friends of yours' (his tone was half-apologetic, half-contemptuous), 'but we do hit it off pretty well, after all—I mean, we like the same sort of things, riding and so on, and —oh, sod it,' he broke off, 'I can't say properly what I want to say, but you know what I mean.'

For a moment I could say nothing, struck dumb by Gerald's extraordinary outburst. My mind was a chaos of conflicting feelings: half-amused, half-touched, I was aware also of a sense of release, as though some obstruction in my mind had been suddenly removed.

'Yes,' I said at last, 'I think I understand.'

'Well, that's O.K. then,' Gerald exclaimed, brushing aside the subject with the brusque air of a chairman at a board-meeting disposing of some tiresome though essential item on the agenda. 'Let's have the other half—come on, drink up.'

'I'll be tight,' I protested.

'Never mind—does you good, once in a way,' Gerald grinned.

About the rest of that evening I remember very little; I know only that, by the time we staggered into the street at closing-time, I was in no state to go home by myself, and had to be escorted back to college by Gerald. I remember, too, that before we parted we had sworn vows of eternal friendship —or at any rate I had; Gerald, I suspect, had contented himself with shaking hands and muttering something about 'everything being O.K. now'. We had arranged, also, to resume our riding: Gerald had promised to book our horses, if possible, for the very next day. I tumbled into bed, at last, with a feeling that a new phase of my life had begun: at last —so I assured myself, as I drifted towards sleep—at long last

I had escaped from my imprisoning Ego into the adult and exciting world of Real Life.

Real Life, alas, on the following morning, manifested itself in a form which I found too realistic by half: I woke with a splitting headache, and, having managed to stagger as far as the college bathroom, proceeded to be violently and embarrassingly sick.

After a bath and breakfast, however, I felt considerably better, and more able to confront the demands of the Reality Principle. I spent the morning at Acott's, listening to gramophone records of Debussy and Delius; returning to college, I found a note from Gerald saying that the horses were booked for that afternoon at half-past two.

The ride that afternoon was the first of many such outings, and it was, I think, during the next few weeks, that my friendship with Gerald attained to its happiest and most intimate phase. At first, it is true, I suffered from a slight sense of anticlimax: for Gerald's friendship didn't, after all, make me feel notably more 'real' than I had felt before. Yet the more I saw of him, the more likeable I found him: I began to accept him for what he was—an ordinary, unexciting but extremely nice person; and in a sense, I suppose, our association did, after all, aspire to that long-sought and ill-defined ideal of 'Reality' for which Gerald had seemed to provide so appropriate a symbol.

During the rest of that term, we spent a good deal of time together: sometimes I would visit Gerald at his rooms, sometimes we would meet at the Clarendon. He introduced me to one or two of his acquaintances—fellow-medical students, for the most part: pleasant enough, if a trifle dull, they seemed to have little importance in Gerald's life, and it struck me, for the first time, that Gerald was a surprisingly lonely person. I say 'surprisingly', for Gerald, after all, was not unsociable, nor was he lacking in charm; moreover, he played rugger, boxed occasionally, and belonged to one or two of the university clubs. Yet none of his social contacts seemed more than superficial; his attitude towards most of his acquaintances was one of mild and tolerant contempt. He despised what he called my 'smarty-arty' friends; but he seemed scarcely less censorious about people in his own circle. In his own way, I think, he was a perfectionist: he demanded certain qualities in people which they too seldom possessed, and he wasn't prepared (as I, alas, too often was) to make do with second-best. He wanted friendship—wanted it, perhaps, as much as I did—but it must be all or nothing: he wouldn't accept any sort of compromise, and a certain native pride made him scrupulous in concealing his emotional needs. The quality of self-sufficiency, inherited from his midland working-class forebears, afforded him a protection which was sadly lacking in myself, and which I secretly envied; Gerald, on occasion, could be hard, but he was never arrogant; his pride was offset by a natural humility which tempered even his harshest judgments with an element of forebearance. Thus, having roundly condemned some too-beautiful aesthete (an acquaintance of mine, as it happened) as a 'bloody nancy-boy', he would add, with a tolerant grin: 'Of course, you can't blame him, really—a bloke like that must have some sort of kink: something to do with his glands, probably—and come to that, we're all of us a bit homo when it comes to the point.'

As for women, Gerald viewed them with much the same tolerant disdain as he showed towards his male friends and towards the world in general. Like food, they were a physiological necessity—and about food (though he enjoyed it well enough) Gerald was not, as I had often noticed, over-particular. 'They're all the same in the dark,' he would say, or: 'I don't let them worry me much, but a chap's got to have his oats.' His attitude in this matter as in others seemed to me enviably adult, though the details of his conquests, when he related them, struck me as being squalid and rather tedious. Gerald, for his part, displayed little curiosity about my own amorous problems; on at least one occasion, however, I must have hinted, rather too obviously, at my private difficulties, for I found, to my horror, that Gerald—without consulting me—had arranged a joint outing with Gladys and Kathleen from the Clarendon ('It'll take you out of yourself,' said Gerald, with an avuncular benevolence). We were to take them to the cinema in the afternoon: 'And after that,' said Gerald, 'it's up to you: they have to back be at the Clarry at six o'clock, but I usually arrange to meet Kathleen at closing time, and take her home. She's rather sweet on me at the moment, so I'll leave Gladys to you, if you've no objection.'

I was appalled; but there seemed no possible escape. To back out at this stage would seem not only rude but ungrateful: for Gerald, I couldn't help feeling, had fixed up the jaunt entirely for my benefit. It was, I supposed, a kind of test of my virility: if I didn't go through with it, Gerald would despise me; and I valued Gerald's opinion, in such matters, more than I would have cared to admit.

We duly met the two girls, when the bar closed after lunch, and escorted them to the Super Cinema. I bought Gladys a box of chocolates, and, being well-fortified with beer, managed to adopt what I hoped was a suitably rakish manner. Gladys, for her part, behaved with a lady-like refinement which was calculated to discourage a far more hot-blooded lover than myself; when at last the lights went down and the film started, I heaved a sigh of relief; at least, I thought, one wouldn't be expected to talk. But what, I asked myself with growing horror, exactly what, in the circumstances, *was* one expected to do? I had gathered—partly from observation, partly from contemporary novels—that one began by holding hands. . . . Tremulously, in the darkness, I edged my hand towards the spot where I supposed Gladys's hand to be; this opening gambit, however, was singularly inefficacious, for Gladys's hand proved to be grasping the box of chocolates. Supposing, very naturally, that the chocolates were what I was after, she thrust the box towards me; I clutched at it, but, in my extreme nervousness, contrived to drop it. Box and chocolates cascaded into the darkness at our feet: trembling with shame, I leaned forward and fumbled awkwardly in the narrow space between the seats; having managed to rescue at least some of the chocolates, I kept the box, this time, upon my own knee, and, after muttering my apologies, fixed my attention firmly upon the screen, where Ramon Novarro was engaged in passionately embracing a young woman whose plump cheeks were copiously gemmed with more than life-size glycerine tears. The moment seemed propitious for a renewed assault on my part; and once again I extended my hand, timorously, in the direction of Gladys. This time she did not misinterpret my intention, and immediately grasped my hand in a firm and somewhat sticky grip; I returned the pressure, less firmly, perhaps, but (I hoped) quite unequivocally. Gladys's eyes were fixed resolutely upon the screen: in the half-darkness I could just see her face—severe and matronly as the Demeter of Cnidos. Plainly she was far more interested in Ramon Novarro than in myself, and no wonder; she continued, none the less, to clasp my hand in a firm, enveloping grip which seemed not so much amorous as protective. I was reminded, indeed, of those occasions, in my childhood, when my Nannie, knowing that I was frightened of the dark, used to hold my hand during the showing of the magic lantern in the nursery.

Gladys, however, I reminded myself, was not a Nannie but (in the specialized and venal sense of the word) a Woman; and I knew that with Women one was expected to do rather more than just hold their hands. In comparable situations, in novels, young men's hands were apt to stray 'with apparent casualness' to other and more intimate parts of the female anatomy; but in the present circumstances this seemed much less easy of accomplishment than one might have supposed. For one thing, Gladys appeared to be quite genuinely absorbed in the film; for another, her hand continued to clasp mine with such a nannie-like firmness that it seemed almost impossible to withdraw it, without resorting to downright violence. Moreover, even supposing that I had been able to free my hand, I should have felt extremely uncertain as to which portion of Gladys's somewhat abundant anatomy to explore next; parts of it, I felt, were altogether too 'intimate', others perhaps not intimate enough. And in any case (I thought) Gladys herself showed no apparent desire for such explorations; she seemed perfectly content with her chocolates and with Ramon Novarro who, stripped to the waist and looking extremely handsome, now appeared to be bravely defending the heroine (registering 'horror', with her fist thrust firmly into her mouth) against a horde of hostile savages.

I had seldom, in my whole life, felt quite so miserable; but worse was to follow. The beer, with which I had managed to fortify (though imperfectly) my somewhat flaccid libido, now began to have other and less happy effects. For the next twenty minutes or so I managed to ignore the increasing discomfort; but Nature, at last, refused to be denied. Discomfort became agony: yet I dared not leave my seat. Conventions were stricter, at that period, than they are today: lavatories were presumed, for social purposes, not to exist; and I was, perhaps, more than normally sensitive in such matters. We were, furthermore, wedged firmly in the middle of the stalls, with at least a dozen pairs of legs between us and the gangway. Escape seemed impossible: I sweated, I began incontinently to fidget; and still Gladys kept my hand imprisoned, relentlessly, in hers. At last I could bear it no longer: muttering something about 'a breath of fresh air' I disengaged my hand, rose awkwardly to my feet, and stumbled past our indignant neighbours to the gangway.

Once outside, I was tempted to leave the cinema and return, ignominiously, to my rooms: I could always say that I had been taken ill—and indeed, at that moment, I was quite prepared to take to my bed for a week merely to substantiate my own story. Finally I decided to compromise, and stood up, uncomfortably, in the gangway, until the interval. The film dragged to its end at last, and I returned, covered with blushes, to my seat, to find Gladys engaged in an animated conversation with Gerald, and apparently not in the least perturbed by my absence. The lights went down again, and the second film began—a slapstick comedy featuring Harold Lloyd; on this occasion I made no attempt to renew my amorous advances; nor, to my relief, did Gladys offer me the slightest encouragement.

At last it was over, and we got up to go. My humiliation, I felt, was complete: and I carefully avoided Gerald's eyes as we made our way out into the foyer. Gerald, however, seemed perfectly unaware of the ordeal to which I had been subjected;

waiting at the entrance, while the girls went to 'powder their noses', he winked at me conspiratorially.

'Old Gladys all right?' he asked.

I replied, with a feeble attempt to maintain my rakish pose, that I thought Gladys 'very nice'. At that moment I almost hated Gerald—hated him for his presumption, his obtuseness, and what seemed to me a gross lack of sensibility. My own humiliation, my sense of my own inadequacy, were suddenly kindled into a hot, vicious flame of hostility; with anybody but Gerald, I should without a doubt have lost my temper. Fortunately, I managed to check myself; the girls returned, and, as we accompanied them down the Cornmarket towards the Clarendon, I felt thankful that I had curbed my anger. The afternoon had been appalling; yet somehow, after that brief spurt of malice, I couldn't bring myself to blame Gerald; and I knew that, when it came to the point, I valued his friendship too highly to risk an open quarrel.

A week or two after this intimidating experience, Gerald and I went out riding. It was a day in early March, one of those brilliant, spring-like days which sometimes occur, miraculously, after a long spell of bad weather. We rode out, as usual, towards Godstow: the hedgerows and copses were furred with purple buds, coltsfoot and celandines blazed in the ditches. I noticed that Gerald, despite the fine weather, seemed in rather low spirits; he looked pale and drawn, and presently confessed that he had been working harder than usual. Apparently, too, he was having some sort of 'trouble' with his family—his father, I gathered, considered that Gerald was living too expensively, and had threatened to cut down his allowance.

'It's a bit tough,' Gerald commented, in that off-hand

manner with which he habitually spoke of his own affairs. 'After all, I only came up to this lousy place to please him; and I'm not really an extravagant sort of bloke—my digs are about as cheap as you could find, and I don't have expensive tastes. What I mean is, a pint or two of an evening, and a bit of slap-and-tickle with Kathleen now and again—it's not a hell of a lot to ask, after all.'

Gerald fell silent, and, though I tried to keep up the conversation, seemed reluctant to pursue the subject. I had, as it happened, picked up quite a lot of information about Gerald's family during recent conversations with him, and what I had heard didn't sound very pleasant. The Brockhursts, I guessed, were both dim and pretentious: petty burgesses, newly enriched, and afflicted by the nastiest and most boring kind of snobbery. I could imagine, only too well, their 'place' in Surrey—somewhere between Woking and Camberley: a red Edwardian house among pine-trees, with a laurelled drive in front and a tennis-court at the back. Gerald's father was a great golfer, and the house was convenient for the links; his wife, it seemed was a Christian Scientist—a fact to which Gerald referred with a slightly pitying contempt, rather as though his mother suffered from 'nerves', or some minor but embarrassing skin-disease. There was an elder brother named Kenneth, at present coffee-planting in Kenya, and a sister, Sheila, who had some sort of secretarial job in London; Gerald didn't seem particularly attached to either of them. Kenneth, it appeared, was the family favourite, and had already come into more than his fair share of the family fortune—the result, in part, of Gerald's decision to take up medicine against his father's wishes. In the circumstances, I couldn't help admiring the tolerant good nature with which Gerald regarded his brother and, indeed, his whole family.

'The fact is,' he said to me on one occasion, 'I'm the family blacksheep. I always have been, and I suppose I always shall be. The pater was all for Ken from the start, and so was mother, and what with him and Sheila, I never got a proper look-in.'

Myself the runt of the litter, I could entirely sympathize, and said so; though Gerald was the last person I should ever have suspected of being a 'blacksheep'.

'Oh, I don't blame them,' Gerald went on, tolerantly. 'I suppose I'll get a little when the old man kicks the bucket, but I don't care much, either way. I'm glad I'll be independent, really—it's better that way, if you can manage it.'

'You're telling me,' I said, with feeling. I envied Gerald's independence as I envied his strength and stability. Of all the people I knew, he seemed the most securely armed against the world; there was something solid and unshakable about him which reminded me of those Russian toys, carved and painted to resemble *moujiks*, with a lead weight at the bottom, which, as often as one tries to knock them over, bob up again, serene and invincible, to face a fresh assault. Gerald, I thought, would never let life 'get him down'; whatever misfortunes he might encounter, he would, one felt, take them in his stride. He had his weaknesses—beer and (to a lesser extent) women, but I couldn't imagine that either of these would ever constitute a serious threat to his integrity. Some day, I supposed, he would fall in love and marry—a nice sensible girl who shared his tastes and his modest ambitions; it would all be rather un-romantic, but eminently suitable and cosy; they would settle (I decided) somewhere in the home-counties, and Gerald would ask me to be godfather to his children.

We rode, as usual, round the meadows, cantering for short distances on the dry stretches between the flooded levels. The sunshine, the keen March wind had induced in me a mood of gay irresponsibility: I decided that I would take Gerald out to dinner that night, and that we would get gloriously tight. Gerald himself, after a brisk canter or two, seemed in better spirits: 'There's nothing like it for shaking up the old liver,' he remarked. 'To tell you the truth, I wasn't feeling too good when we started out, but I'm feeling on top of the bloody world, now.'

Riding back, leisurely, through the fields, we came to a lonely backwater, half-hidden from view by pollard-willows. Suddenly Gerald pulled up his horse.

'Tell you what,' he exclaimed, 'let's have a swim.'

'Not on your life,' I said. 'The water'll be icy.'

'Ballocks to that,' Gerald retorted. 'The sun's lovely and warm—do you a world of good. Come on, you sissy old bastard.'

'I'm not quite dotty,' I replied. 'You bathe if you want to, but you won't get me in.'

We had pulled up our horses at the edge of the backwater and Gerald had already dismounted.

'You're coming in,' he said, peremptorily, scowling up at me with a sudden, half-playful ferocity.

'I'm not.'

'You bloody well are.'

'I tell you I'm not.'

'I'll bloody well force you to.'

'You won't.'

'Oh, come on, be a sport: just in and out—you'll feel grand after it.'

I protested that I hated the cold and wasn't going to risk pneumonia; Gerald, however, with an unaccustomed obstinacy, continued to badger me. His voice had taken on a curiously urgent tone, as though the question of whether I bathed or not were a matter of life or death; puzzled, I looked down at his scowling face, and wondered what exactly was in his mind. I had no intention of bathing; yet I felt, absurdly, that I was being subjected to some obscure and arbitrary test of loyalty. It was unlike Gerald to be so importunate; and I couldn't help suspecting that, consciously or otherwise, he had invested the occasion with some private and wholly disproportionate significance.

'Oh, all right then,' he said at last, 'if you won't you won't.'

His voice was suddenly sharp with exasperation, and as I met his eyes I could see that he was genuinely angry. With an impatient movement, he flung his horse's reins across my saddle.

'Here, hold my horse, then—I'm going in, even if you won't.'

He began at once to undress, stripping off his clothes with a curious air of urgency, almost of desperation, as though he were about to perform some heroic feat of life-saving. His face was still a sullen mask: I knew that, in some inexplicable way, I had deeply offended him, and for a moment I was half-tempted to change my mind and bathe after all. Yet the thought of the icy river-water held me back: I wasn't, when it came to the point, prepared to risk catching a chill merely to gratify a passing whim of Gerald's.

With a final, violent movement, he pulled his shirt over his head, and stood for a moment, naked, his arms hugged across his chest, the wind faintly stirring his short rumpled hair. Red-brown at the throat and wrists, the rest of his body was of a matt, milky whiteness: his nakedness seemed strangely incongruous and rather shocking against the background of this bleak wintry landscape. I watched him crouch forward, like a sprinter at the start of a race, the muscles rippling beneath his firm white flesh; for a moment he paused, balanced on his haunches; then, with a sudden savage shout like a battle-cry, he dashed down the grassy bank, raised his arms, and dived cleanly into the steel-blue, sunbright water. For several seconds I watched the ripples spread upon the waveless surface; suddenly panic gripped me: perhaps the pool was shallower than it appeared, perhaps Gerald had been seized by cramp.... A moment later I saw his head emerge, a dark blob amid the sun-dazzle, twenty yards from shore. His hair hung in a grotesque fringe over his eyes; he tossed it back, treading water; then raised his arm and hailed me.

'Come on in,' he shouted, 'it's bloody lovely.'

I waved back, and shook my head discouragingly. Gerald threshed the surface with his legs, raising a fountain of bright foam. Again his voice came, resonant and commanding, across the glittering water.

'Tether the bloody horses and come on in.... Buck up, or you'll lose the sun.... Oh, come *on*, for Christ's sake....'

I shook my head again, and saw Gerald turn and swim vigorously away towards the opposite bank. Once again, I had the odd feeling that the whole occasion was in some way crucial, climacteric: it was as though life—in the shape of Gerald—was making some vast, implacable demand upon me which I knew that I couldn't satisfy. Once more, I felt the temptation to strip off my clothes and (risking pneumonia) plunge into the icy water; the impulse was accompanied by a perverse, almost erotic feeling of excitement; yet I knew that I couldn't do it. Over-cossetted in childhood, I was terrified of illness in general and of catching cold in particular. I knew that I lacked the guts to strip and swim in an English river in March; and I knew too, intuitively yet with no less certainty, that, because of my defection, because I had failed to pass the 'test', my relations with Gerald would never be quite the same again.

Sadly I watched him swim back to shore: a few yards from the bank, he began to thresh his limbs about, naïvely showing off for my benefit. I wished, by now, that I had taken the risk and bathed; but it was too late now. Gerald clambered up the muddy bank: I could see that his body was pocked with goose-flesh, and that he was shivering. He dabbed himself, inadequately, with a handkerchief, and scrambled rapidly into his clothes.

'Getting a bit nippy,' he remarked, as he pulled on his breeches; and indeed, though I had scarcely noticed it, a cloud had covered the westering sun, and a chilly wind had risen.

Gerald mounted his horse, and we rode back, almost in silence, along the tow-path. As we reached the town's outskirts, it began to rain—a cold, sleety downpour blowing straight in our faces. At the stables I remembered my plan to take Gerald out to dinner; but the mood of elation which had prompted the idea seemed already to belong to some remote, irrecoverable past. None the less, I proffered the suggestion: impelled less, perhaps, by convivial motives than by an obscure sense of guilt, a desire to make up to Gerald, in some way, for my own shortcomings.

'Not tonight, thanks all the same,' Gerald replied, in a curiously flat, conventional tone. 'Fact is, I really ought to do some work. Sorry, old boy—another time.'

I glanced at him with sudden disquiet: his face wore a remote, preoccupied expression, and he looked, as I had observed before, unusually pale. Nor was it usual for Gerald to address me as 'old boy', a hearty locution which (as I had often noticed) he was accustomed to employ only with comparative strangers, or in situations which required the exercise of a rather forced and bogus magnanimity—as, for example, when somebody trod on his toe in a crowded bar. In its present context, the phrase carried a wounding implication of indifference, perhaps even of hostility; and I parted from Gerald sadly, aware that I had offended him, yet unable—or perhaps unwilling—to analyse precisely the nature or extent of my offence. We hadn't, as we usually did, made a date for our next meeting: 'See you again soon,' Gerald had said, offhandedly, and without his usual smile; and I didn't, at that moment, feel much inclined to press the point.

A week passed—two weeks—and I heard nothing from Gerald. Once again, my latent sense of guilt took the form of a vague hostility, a feeling that Gerald himself was in some way to blame, and that he ought to make the first move. If he was silly enough to take offence merely because I had refused to bathe, that was his look-out. . . . Considered rationally and in retrospect, the whole episode seemed trivial and even laughable; yet my uneasiness persisted, and I knew (however hard I might try to suppress the knowledge) that more had been at stake, on that sunlit afternoon at Godstow, than I was willing to admit.

The weeks slipped away, and still I heard nothing from Gerald. It was not till almost the last day of term that I decided, at last, to go and call on him at his digs.

I was greeted by his landlady with the news that he was in hospital: he had been there nearly a month, with pneumonia.

''E come in one day drenched to the skin,' she related, lugubriously, 'Been out 'orse-riding, 'e 'ad—it must be a month ago almost to the day. Told me 'e'd been swimmin' in the river—'e ought to know better at 'is age,' etc. etc.

I hurried to the hospital, to find that Gerald had been discharged on the previous day. He had been very ill, but had made a remarkably rapid recovery, and had gone home to his family to convalesce.

I meant to write to him, but postponed the task from day to day. The news of his illness had increased my irrational sense of guilt, as though I myself had been in some way to blame: absurd, of course—for had I not warned him of the folly of bathing? And the mere fact of bathing myself, however pleasing to Gerald, could hardly have prevented him from catching pneumonia. I was sorry for him, of course; but there was no denying that I found him a remarkably easy person to banish from my mind. . . . I thought about him more than once during the vac., but with a diminishing enthusiasm; other matters—and other people—claimed my interest. It would be nice to see him again next term—or so I assured myself; in actual fact, I looked forward to our next meeting with considerable disquiet; and perhaps half-hoped, unconsciously, that I should be able to avoid him altogether.

As it happened, I met him within a week or two of the beginning of term. He greeted me with his usual boisterous amiability—perhaps, indeed, he was just a little more boisterous than usual. I apologized for not writing, and for not coming to see him, explaining, rather lamely, that I hadn't known of his illness.

'Oh, that's all right, old boy,' he exclaimed, heartily. 'Glad you've turned up again—let's go and have a drink.'

We went and had a drink—several drinks—at the Clarendon. Gerald chattered away with what for him was an unaccustomed eloquence, telling me about his vac., which had been spent on Exmoor, and about the night-sister at the hospital who, he alleged, had been rather sweet on him, and

whom he had once persuaded to kiss him goodnight. . . .
Gerald, I guessed, was deliberately trying to spare me embarrassment: I was grateful to him, yet I felt sorry that it should
be necessary. His tactfulness was a little too deliberate, a little
too conscious and purposeful: for all his apparent friendliness,
I knew that there was a barrier between us, and that the fault
was mine.

His presence had revived all my old liking for him: I longed
to penetrate his defences, to 'have things out'; but I knew that
Gerald, for the present at any rate, would prefer that I should
remain, as it were, on my own side of the fence. Rather sadly,
I played the game as best I could—laughing at his jokes, and
trying to think of things myself which would amuse him. To
all outward appearance, he seemed perfectly recovered from
his illness: a little thinner, but healthily sunburnt, and with an
undiminished thirst for beer.

During the next few weeks, we met irregularly, and more
or less on the same terms; mostly, I would encounter him in
the Clarendon, and there was a tacit understanding that we
shouldn't—except in the most general terms—refer to the
happenings of the previous term. Our relationship had, in
fact, become a wholly superficial one—an affair of beer,
bawdy talk and a rather too conscious bonhomie; Gerald
didn't come to my digs (I was now living in Beaumont Street),
and I didn't go to his.

I realized that my friendship with him, like so many
previous friendships, had failed; I regretted it, but accepted
the fact—as I had learnt by now to accept such misfortunes
—with a bleak, habitual fatalism. I should have minded more
in earlier days, perhaps; now, however, I had more than
enough friends—or at least acquaintances—to keep my days
well-occupied. I had given up riding, so had Gerald: he was

too busy, he said, working for his schools. As the term went on, I saw less and less of him; and after a time I ceased, except at rare moments of loneliness, to regret his absence.

I saw him for the last time in the Clarendon, just before his schools: he was already rather tight.

'I've been working too hard,' he announced, 'I need a break: I'm going to get properly sozzled. You'd better do the same.'

The evening was a riotous one, and ended—I forget exactly how or why—in somebody's rooms at the House, where, after drinking a quantity of green Chartreuse, I retired somewhat ungracefully into the *Ewigkeit*. I didn't see Gerald again: at the end of the term, I departed for Paris, and returned home to be greeted by the news that I had been sent down. In the months that followed, I lost touch almost entirely with my Oxford friends; and soon Gerald, like the rest, had receded into a past which seemed, already, as remote from my present way of life as the half-remembered events of childhood.

3

After my descent from the university, I worked for the next two years in the book-trade in London. The work bored me, but I wasn't particularly unhappy: I regarded my job, I suppose, as a kind of penance for the follies of Oxford—though such remorse as I felt was occasioned, I fear, less by genuine contrition than by the humiliating feeling that I might, if I had only been more enterprising, have indulged myself far more rewardingly. I couldn't but feel that such a lavish sowing of wild oats ought to have yielded a better crop: I had wasted too much time (I realized it now) on the wrong sort of people—second-rate charmers by whom, in my *naïveté*, I had been too easily beglamoured, and for whom, in reality, I had cared nothing. My time at Oxford had, in fact, been largely spent in a state of almost paranoiac self-delusion: I had thought (at any rate during my last term) that I was enjoying myself; but in reality I had been profoundly miserable.

I felt little regret for Oxford; but in my rare moods of nostalgia, it was Gerald Brockhurst to whom my thoughts would most often return, and I would wonder vaguely what had become of him. It didn't occur to me, however, to write to him for news; for he, like my other friends, had become already a kind of mythical figure, an inhabitant of that remote Olympus from which I myself had been so irrevocably and so ignominiously cast down. I remembered him with a mild elegiac affection tinged by remorse—a kind of Thyrsis, gone with 'the cuckoo's parting cry' into the 'world and wave of men'.

I was, in those days, extremely poor; yet I would contrive, as often as not, to save up a few shillings by the end of the week, and on Saturday night I would wander penuriously round the bars and *boîtes* of the west-end, hopeful of adventure or at least of encountering some acquaintance with more money than myself. Beer was cheap in those days, and one could get a good meal for half-a-crown or three-and-six; one could, moreover, buy a 'rover' ticket for two-and-fourpence at the Alhambra or the Coliseum.

It was on one such Saturday night, nearly two years after leaving Oxford, that, having dined cheaply and in solitude at a restaurant in Lisle Street, I decided to look in at the Alhambra. The theatre was unusually crowded, for Carnera, the giant Italian heavyweight, was billed for a sparring act. Reaching the Circle promenade, I edged my way through the shifting, close-packed crowd towards the front. A chorus-number was in progress: from the bright-lit stage the light was reflected with a vague, hallucinatory effect in the mirrors at the back of the promenade; here and there—in the stage-boxes or in the front row of the circle—a man's shirt-front or a woman's corsage glimmered faint and ghost-like, or a struck match would illuminate, suddenly, the outline of a face, imprinting the unknown features for an instant upon the darkness with the frightening vividness of those flashlight photographs by which some shy nocturnal animal is 'snapped' by the vigilant naturalist. Presently the chorus made their exit, the curtain descended to a blare of music, and rose again to reveal the figures of the Italian boxer and his sparring-partner. Focused by the spotlights, the giant's body seemed curiously unreal, like some top-heavy, ill-constructed model of a man; the performance itself was a farce—the two men danced awkwardly round the stage, tapping at each other in a ludi-crous parody of violence, so that I was reminded of the ballet, *Le Boxing*, a performance of which I had recently seen at the Ballet Club. Around me, in the semi-darkness, the crowd pressed closer towards the balcony; I was aware, beneath the stifling reek of scent and tobacco, of the faint, sour odour of human bodies. Whispered remarks, little snirts of muffled laughter, eddied fitfully among the close-packed ranks; the glow of cigarettes, waxing and waning, lit one intent face after another with a vague rugose light. Half-turning to make my way to the bar, I saw the flare of a match a few feet from where I was standing, and a face was blazoned suddenly upon the darkness—a face which, though it seemed familiar, I couldn't, for a moment, quite place. The match flared again —the man, whoever he was, was smoking a pipe—and once more the features sprang into life: I saw a broad, blunt-featured face, a thatch of hair brushed smoothly back from the forehead. The match went out, the momentary vision was quenched again in the dim, anonymous twilight; but I was almost certain that the face which had gleamed so briefly and so indistinctly in the gloom was the face of Gerald Brockhurst.

The curtain descended, there was a burst of clapping, and I saw the figure of my neighbour move away from the balcony towards the bar. I followed him: for a few seconds, dazzled by the blaze of light after the darkness, I could see nobody who looked in the least like Gerald. Suddenly I felt my arm seized in a violent grip, and turned to see Gerald's face within six inches of my own.

'Well I *am* damned,' he shouted, pumping my hand up and down so violently that it hurt. 'Who'd have thought of seeing *you* here, of all people? It *is* you, isn't it? By God, what a lark —come and have a drink, for Christ's sake.'

The suddenness of the encounter had taken my breath away, and for a moment or two I could scarcely realize Gerald's presence: I was aware only of a figure larger than life, grasping my arm with a policeman-like firmness and propelling me towards the bar. It was not till he had ordered our drinks that Gerald reduced himself, as it were, to manageable proportions.

'Last place I expected to run into you,' he was saying. 'Thought I'd look in to see the boxing—bloody silly show, patting at each other like a couple of kittens—and you could have knocked me down with a feather when I saw you come in. Must be more than two years, isn't it? I was beginning to think you must be dead or something—I'm jolly glad you're not, though.'

Mastering my confusion, I looked for the first time directly at Gerald: he met my eyes with the candid yet faintly mocking gaze which I remembered. His pleasure at meeting me was obviously genuine; and as I looked at him I was overcome by a sudden, paralysing shyness, a sense that whatever I said or did must seem, in the circumstances, hopelessly inadequate. My own pleasure at seeing him was clouded by remorse: my old sense of defection and irrational guilt rose between us like a ghost. Gerald, however, if he noticed my perturbation, firmly disregarded it; and at last, encouraged by his total lack of self-consciousness, I felt my embarrassment suddenly dissipated in a warm impulse of renewed affection. In no time, it seemed, we were talking away as freely as in the first days of our acquaintance; and I knew that I had missed Gerald, during these last two years, more than I had realized.

'By God, we must celebrate,' Gerald exclaimed. 'Have another pint—no, let's have some whisky.'

I explained, with a slight return of my embarrassment, that I was broke: I had, in fact, exactly five shillings in my pocket. Gerald, however, swept my objections aside.

'Ballocks to that,' he retorted. 'I've got enough on me to get us both well and truly plastered—and that, I may tell you, is just what we're going to do.'

He ordered two double whiskies.

'Tell you what,' he suggested, 'let's get out of this place and go to some low dive.'

We went to several low dives: starting at Jack Bloomfield's pub round the corner, and moving on to a squalid and rather sinister club in Soho.

'And now let's have all the dirt,' said Gerald, when we were settled in a corner. 'What have you been up to all these years? Last time *I* saw you, you were passing out on Robin McQueen's floor at the House.'

I gave Gerald a brief account of my own dull doings, and afterwards he told me about himself. He was now at St

Thomas's, and much occupied, at the moment, with mid-wifery cases in the slums of Lambeth. As he talked, I noticed that he seemed more self-confident and, perhaps, a trifle more opinionated than formerly; to look at, he was much the same —a little fuller in the face, but still possessing the healthy, bucolic good-looks of his undergraduate days. As so often in the past, I found myself envying his assurance and aplomb; and, despite his unaffected friendliness, I felt, as ever, a bit at a disadvantage with him. Gerald had always, ever since I had known him, seemed far more mature and 'grown-up' than myself; and I was now, more than ever, struck by his air of comparative adulthood. Gerald, in fact, had now shed the last vestiges of adolescence, and had emerged as a fully-fledged adult male, settled into the job of his choice, and apparently on the best of terms with life. By comparison, I felt myself a pretender—a mere overgrown schoolboy, playing at being grown-up, yet remaining still, to all intents and purposes, *in statu pupillari*.

Gerald was living in digs somewhere in Pimlico; his parents still inhabited their place near Woking. Gerald's relations with his family remained, so I gathered, amicable but a little strained.

'I manage to run down now and again,' he told me. 'As a matter of fact, I've just invested in a car—an awful old bus, I picked it up cheap from a bloke at Thomas's, but it's good enough for the likes of me. Tell you what, I thought of going down next weekend—why don't you come too? Breath of country air'ld do you a world of good.'

In my pleasure at meeting Gerald, and fortified with half-a-dozen whiskies, I was in no state to refuse such an invitation: though from what I remembered of Gerald's account of his family, the weekend hardly promised to be very enjoyable.

'And now,' Gerald announced, 'we're going to get stinking.'

We finished the evening in my bed-sitting-room in the King's Road, Chelsea. Gerald had bought a half-bottle of whisky at the last 'low dive', and we drank it, in turn, out of my tooth-glass. Gerald, rather to my surprise, became extremely drunk; I had seen him imbibe prodigious quantities at Oxford, but I had never before seen him the worse for it. At two o'clock in the morning he still seemed indisposed to go: dead-tired myself, I reminded him of the time, and hoped he would take the hint.

'Oh, sod it,' he protested. Then, glancing at my bed in the corner, he said: 'Can't I doss down here? There's plenty of room for two.'

'I should get home, if I were you,' I said, knowing that Gerald, in his present mood, was quite capable of sitting up for another hour or so. I was afflicted, moreover, by a spinsterly primness in such matters: I hated sharing my bed with anybody else, and I dreaded the crapulous squalor of to-morrow's awakening—lending Gerald my razor, explaining to the landlady, and so forth.

'Oh, all right,' Gerald agreed at last, heaving himself out of his chair. 'I'd better f—— off, in that case.'

His voice had a sharp, resentful note, and I could see that he was offended.

'No, you'd better stay,' I said, impulsively. 'There's plenty of room really, if you don't mind me snoring.'

'No, no, I'll be off.' He moved towards the door; his face was set in a sullen, implacable frown.

'Honestly, I wish you'd stay,' I pleaded, miserable at having offended him.

'Thanks all the same, old boy—cheerioh, and thanks for a nice evening.'

I followed him down the stairs and into the street, where we managed to find a late taxi. He climbed into it without speaking. As the taxi drove off, he put his head through the window and shouted:

'Don't forget you're coming to stay with me for the weekend.'

Three days passed, I heard nothing from Gerald, and concluded (not without a certain relief)that the weekend was off. On the Friday, however, he rang me up: he sounded bluff and amiable as ever, and I knew that I was forgiven. Petty enough in itself, my prim refusal to put Gerald up for the night had, as I very well realized, provoked him to one of those sudden, inexplicable fits of resentment which I remembered from the past; and I was reminded, with a stab of nostalgia, of that March afternoon at Godstow when I had refused to bathe.

I met Gerald on the following day in a pub at Victoria, and in the afternoon we drove down, in a battered old Morris, to his home. It was a bright day in early autumn, and I was glad enough to escape from London, if it were only into the coniferous glooms of darkest Surrey. Gerald was in a gay, irresponsible mood; and I myself should have felt happy enough, but for my growing alarm at the prospect of meeting his family, whom I had every reason to suppose I should dislike; nor, indeed, were my fears to prove unjustified.

At Woking, we ran into rain, and arrived at Gerald's home, unpropitiously, in a downpour. I had imagined the house a red, Edwardian villa among pines; it proved to be a rather bleak-looking affair in stockbroker's Tudor, built, I suppose, in about 1924, and separated from its nearly identical neighbours by thickets of silver birch. The house was called

'Burnbrae'; a Sealyham yapped menacingly at us on the doorstep; in the hall, the fumed-oak fireplace was inscribed with a quotation from Omar Khayyam in Gothic script; and from the ceiling hung an enormous wrought-iron lantern in the Hollywood-baronial style. We were received, rather off-handedly, by Gerald's sister, Sheila—a dark-browed, angry-looking girl who, I was convinced, loathed me at sight. Tea was ready, and we went into the drawing-room (Waring and Gillow, with 'jazz' cushions), where Mrs Brockhurst presided over an elaborate tea-tray, flanked by plates of exquisitely thin sandwiches and rather nasty-looking cakes; Mr Brockhurst, it seemed, was on the golf-links. Gerald's mother reminded me of the Cheshire cat: her smile—the persistent, hypnotic smile of the Christian Scientist—seemed to exist, so to speak, *in vacuo*, independently of the vague, characterless features which framed it. For the rest, she seemed amiable enough, if a little insipid; as we drank our tea, she kept up an intermittent fire of trivial and singularly pointless questions, mostly directed at myself: what was the weather like in London yesterday, did I prefer travelling by tube or bus, did I know Chiswick (where an aunt of hers, long dead and apparently unregretted, had once lived)—etc. etc. Sheila, I noticed, was inclined to bully her mother, and seemed chronically discontented with her family and, indeed, with life in general; her conversation consisted almost entirely of complaints—of the tea, of the weather, of her work in London, of the hostel where she lodged, of the plays or films which she had lately seen. Things or persons of which or of whom she disapproved were invariably described as 'absolutely foul'; anything unusual or outside her extremely narrow range of appreciation, was 'frightfully weird' or (with a deprecating little laugh) 'rather too highbrow for *me*, I'm afraid.' I disliked her as much as she only too obviously disliked me; partly to show my disapproval, partly out of pity for her victim, I tried to be as nice as possible to Mrs Brockhurst. My attempts to 'draw her out' were, however, notably unsuccessful: the more I talked, the more remotely unapproachable did she become, retreating behind her handsome and lavishly displayed dentures like some timid mollusc into the interior of its shell.

It was a considerable relief when Major Brockhurst (for thus he styled himself) returned from the links. I had been puzzled by the total lack of family likeness between Gerald and his mother and sister; it was now evident that Gerald took after his father, though even here the affinity was not markedly apparent. The Major (he had acquired some kind of temporary rank during the war, and still jealously retained it) looked what he was: a tough midland business-man who had done well out of the war, but not quite well enough. Beneath his bluff, slightly pompous façade, one could see that he was disgruntled and ill-at-ease, a man's man who, retired too early, was inclined to chafe at the padded, female ambience of his home. Plainly he was doing his best to live up to his honorary rank of Major and to the upper middle-class background which the title implied; yet his Harris tweed coat and knickerbockers and cloth cap seemed subtly wrong, the midland accent betrayed itself through the haw-haw of the stage colonel, and one felt that the assumed rôle was a perpetual effort, with which Major Brockhurst was becoming, already, just a trifle bored.

Presently Gerald suggested a 'run in the car' before dinner —an invitation which he accompanied by a significant wink at me. We drove to a pub a few miles away and drank beer.

'I'm afraid you won't get much at dinner-time,' Gerald

apologized. 'Mother doesn't approve, you see, being a Christian Scientist, and the pater doesn't go beyond a couple of whiskies.'

The beer proved, indeed, to be a wise precaution, for dinner that night was a surprisingly inadequate affair—soup (obviously tinned) followed by cold beef and salad, carefully doled out by Mrs Brockhurst, whose smile, as she carved up the scraggy remnant of a sirloin, seemed to become more intense, more dazzlingly spiritual than ever. One was made to feel that the mere fact of taking nourishment was a regrettable (if necessary) concession to Mortal Mind; and we were not offered a second helping.

The next day, Sunday, was wet; at half-past ten, Mrs Brockhurst set off for the Christian Science church in Camberley, escorted with evident reluctance by her husband, a recent and somewhat half-hearted convert to the cult. Sheila spent the morning in what she ferociously described as 'stripping the Sealyham'; Gerald and I drove out to the pub at midday and drank beer among a crowd of pink, yapping subalterns.

'I'm afraid you're finding all this a crashing bore,' Gerald apologized, adding, with a shy smile: 'It's jolly nice of you to have come, anyway.'

'I'm not in the least bored,' I assured him—and oddly enough it was more than half true; for the Brockhurst *ménage* had begun to exercise a fascination of horror, I was both appalled and, in a curious way, attracted. I don't know quite what I had expected of Gerald's family; but the reality was certainly at variance with my anticipations. I had, I think, imagined the Brockhursts to be much more vulgarly prosperous, and it had surprised me to find that they were so unostentatious and, comparatively speaking, so poor. Not till long after did I hear that the Major had, in fact, lost a good deal of money since his retirement; he had wished to sell the house and buy a smaller one in a cheaper neighbourhood, but Mrs Brockhurst, with Christianly Scientific optimism, had refused to hear of it. The need for retrenchment appealed to her natural parsimoniousness, and, like so many middle-class women of her type, she was gallantly prepared to starve not only herself but the rest of her family rather than relinquish the outward trappings of gentility. It was hardly surprising that Gerald should spend as little time as possible at home; and I could only admire the tolerant, easy-going attitude which he adopted towards his parents and his sister. It was easy to see that he had little genuine affection for his family; yet his behaviour to his mother and father remained —unlike that of Sheila—impeccably restrained and courteous.

Sunday lunch—roast beef and apple pie—was a slight improvement upon the previous night's dinner, in quality if not in quantity. The Major even produced, with an air of reckless conviviality, a half-bottle of inferior Graves for Gerald and me (he drank a small whisky-and-water himself). Afterwards, since it continued to rain, we sat in the bleak, unheated drawing-room, dozing over the Sunday papers. (The Major unashamedly covered his face with the *Observer* and snored.)

Gerald and I motored up to London after tea. Driving through the darkening countryside and the outlying suburbs, gleaming under the rain and loud with church-bells, I thought of the weekend, already, with the kind of perverse nostalgia with which one remembers an illness or some youthful unhappiness. Gerald's family background, if unenviable, had acquired for me a kind of poetry of its own: it was linked with Sapper's novels, old *Strand Magazine* stories by Wodehouse or Gilbert Frankau—a whole world of heroic phantasy which, in my prep. school days, had epitomized for me the mysterious and rather frightening prospect of being 'grown-up', and which now seemed bodied forth in the Brockhurst family and, to some degree, in the person of Gerald himself. The Brockhursts conformed perfectly to type, and, in a world in which such conformity was becoming increasingly rare, seemed to me to possess (like some primitive tribe which retains its customs and taboos despite the encroachments of an alien culture) an integrity which was lacking in most of the people I knew, and which, in a perverse and half-reluctant way, I admired.

4

My intermittent, rather uneasy friendship with Gerald was now once again resumed. Often I would meet him for a drink in a favourite pub of his at Lambeth, not far from St Thomas's; and one Saturday afternoon I went and watched him playing rugger for the hospital against Bart's. Our relationship had become a casual, comradely affair, without commitments on either side; Gerald, like myself, was lonely—he seemed by nature a man of few friends—and we were glad enough of one another's company. The barrier which had fallen between us during that last term at Oxford was, as I was dimly aware, still there; but I had long since relinquished any idea of a more intimate relation with Gerald, and I was perfectly prepared to accept him on his own terms. My feeling for him, at this time, was in fact rather of the sort which doggy people have for their favourite pet: I enjoyed his company, but I didn't expect him to share my interests; nor did it occur to me (and in this I differed from most dog-lovers) to introduce him to my other friends. I valued him, indeed, largely because of his refreshing unlikeness to most of the people I knew; very few of my acquaintances, I felt, would share my penchant for Gerald's amiable philistinism, still less would they appreciate his *Strand Magazine* background which, for me, provided an additional—if somewhat perverse—attraction. I preferred to keep my friendship with him a secret, rather as I might have concealed the fact that I was an impenitent addict of *Bulldog Drummond* or the novels of Dornford Yates.

Sometimes Gerald and I would meet for dinner and go to a cinema or a music-hall, finishing up (if we could afford it) at the Criterion brasserie or the Café Royal. It was on one such occasion that, greatly daring, I conceived the unlucky idea of taking Gerald to the Blue Lantern, of which I had lately become a member. I was naïvely proud of belonging to a Real Nightclub, and liked showing it off: I ought, of course, to have realized that the Lantern wasn't Gerald's cup of tea at all; he wouldn't feel at ease, and might easily be offended by the manners of the *habitués*, who belonged, for the most part, to the raffish fringes of that pseudo-'smart' Bohemia which was perhaps the most characteristic (and almost certainly the nastiest) social unit of that period. I ought to have known better: yet the idea of Gerald in such a milieu appealed to my taste for the incongruous; nor, perhaps, was I wholly innocent of a mischievous desire to *épater le bourgeois*—though Gerald, as I knew by now, despite certain well-defined prejudices, was by no means easy to shock.

The Blue Lantern that evening was quite as beastly as usual, and perhaps even beastlier. Gerald and I sat at a corner table downstairs and drank lager. Hugh Wade, the pianist, accompanied by drums and a saxophone, was discoursing the half-forgotten, nostalgic tunes of the first-war period; the dance-floor was crowded with painted and twittering young men whose partners, though technically of the female sex (for the Lantern was rather fussy about such conventions), appeared for the most part to be a good deal more virile than their cavaliers.

'God, what an awful crowd,' said Gerald. 'Tell you what, let's go round to the Forty-Three—I can always get in there, I know Ma Merrick. It's a stinking hole, but it doesn't stink as bad as this joint.'

By way of a compromise, I suggested going upstairs and having a drink at the bar. No sooner had we sat down and ordered our drinks than I heard a female voice addressing me by my Christian name, and turned to find myself face to face with Veriny Crighton-Jones.

'My dear,' she exclaimed, in her fashionably husky voice, 'it's utter heaven to see you. That *monster* Bertie Westmacott was meeting me, and I've been waiting here at *least* a thousand years, and I'm madly depressed. Do buy me a drink—here's some money, I know you're broke—and please introduce me to your boy-friend at *once*, I think he's a perfect lamb, and I'd like to eat him, d'you think he'd mind?'

It was thus, unavoidably and in the least propitious of circumstances, that I introduced Gerald to Veriny Crighton-Jones. I had known Veriny for some years: we had met, incongruously enough, at Bedales, where she had come, with her parents, to visit a cousin, who happened to be a friend of mine. I had immediately conceived a violent though almost wholly platonic passion for her: for Veriny, at that time, had seemed to me to typify the kind of woman whom I most fervently admired—a type which, it should be added, I had so far encountered only in fiction.

Veriny was strikingly beautiful in a style then becoming

fashionable (the 'waif,' or *gamine*), and which, a few years later, would find its popular prototype in the *faux-naïf*, elfin charm of Fraülein Elisabeth Bergner. With her boyish figure, her blonde Eton crop and her street-arab's grin, Veriny not unnaturally seemed to me to belong to a wholly different species from the sort of girl to whom, at Bedales and in my home circle, I had been accustomed. There was something about her, I liked to think, of the Constant Nymph—an air of apparent innocence masking an illimitable sophistication (or did I, perhaps, mean the other way round?); her husky voice strongly suggested the 'death-bed' articulation of Mrs Viveash in *Antic Hay*, and her morals, from all I had heard about them, invited comparison with those of Iris Storm, that 'shameful, shameless lady' of Michael Arlen's celebrated novel. It seemed safe to infer, at least, that she had a number of lovers; probably she was a nymphomaniac, and quite possibly a drug-addict into the bargain. . . . In the novel which I immediately began to write about her, after her first visit to the school, she was all these things and more; and the sequel was to prove that Nature, in most respects (as is her habit), had once again imitated Art.

Like Firbank's Miss Sinquier, Veriny was the daughter of a country parson, who had outraged her family by 'going on the stage'. At the time I first met her, she was still at the R.A.D.A.; by the time I encountered her again in London, she had graduated to the chorus of the Cochran revue at the Pavilion; and, at the period when I introduced her to Gerald, she had lately scored a minor success in *revue intime* at the Little Theatre.

Veriny, if she didn't altogether live up to my idea of her as a nymphomaniac, certainly possessed (as I soon discovered) an embracing and, on the whole, undiscriminating fondness for young men. There was no conclusive evidence to show that she drugged; but she certainly drank like a fish, and, moreover, had learnt to hold her liquor a good deal better than most of her (or my own) male acquaintances. I should hardly have supposed that she was Gerald's cup of tea; indeed, I fully expected him to be as shocked by her behaviour as he had been by the antics of the dancers on the floor below. To my astonishment, however, it was perfectly evident that he found her irresistible; soon, indeed, I began to feel that my presence was superfluous, and wandered downstairs. Returning a quarter of an hour later, I saw that they were already shamelessly holding hands, and that Gerald was gazing into her eyes with a besotted, cow-like expression of which I should never before have supposed him capable.

Later, we all returned to the dance-room, and I sat, disconsolately, at a corner table, watching them as they danced. They made a handsome couple, I thought: and as I watched them I was overcome by a wild despairing envy of their beauty and of the shared happiness which transfigured their faces. Doomed, myself (as I was convinced), to a perpetual, frustrated celibacy, I could only wonder at the freakish ways of Providence, which had decreed that it should be myself, of all people, who had brought about this meeting. The sensation was, for that matter, all too familiar; for, on more than one occasion of late, I had found myself in precisely the same situation. I was destined, it seemed, to the perpetual rôle of unofficial (and unwitting) pander among the friends to whom I was most attached; in the chemistry of Love, my function was that of the catalyst—inert, sluggish, without inherent power of action, yet capable (it seemed) of precipitating the most violent and complex reactions in my immediate vicinity.

Presently, when Gerald and Veriny returned to our table, I said I was tired and wanted to go home.

'But my dears, you absolutely *must* come and have a drink with me,' Veriny insisted. 'They're just closing here' (the Lantern was strict about licensing hours), 'and I've got a delicious bottle of whisky and loads of gin.'

At any other time, I should probably have accepted this invitation; Veriny lived in a flat in St John's Wood, and I knew, from past experience, that her parties were apt (when she was 'resting', as she was at present) to be quite uninhibited, and to prolong themselves well into the small hours. Tonight, however, it was only too evident that I should be in the way; even as she spoke, Veriny was grasping Gerald's hand, possessively, beneath the table. My function as catalyst was, I decided with melancholy resignation, at an end; and I had no desire to assist at the chemical process which my introduction had so fatally initiated.

'Oh well, *you'll* come, won't you, my sweet?' Veriny said, turning to Gerald, and speaking in her huskiest, most Arlenish tones.

We left the club at last; Gerald and Veriny drove off in a taxi; and I was left to make my own way, solitary and disconsolate, along the empty reaches of Piccadilly towards my cheerless bed-sitting-room in the King's Road.

I saw nothing of Gerald for a fortnight or so: at the end of a week I rang him up and suggested a meeting, but he pleaded a previous engagement—I could guess only too easily with whom.

'Sorry, old boy' (I recognized the familiar, off-putting locution), 'I can't make it that night. Fact is, I'm meeting a dame.'

'Oh, you are, are you,' I said. Gerald's tone, over the telephone, had an assumed casualness beneath which I could detect a note of purring complacency. 'I suppose,' I added, guessing that he would be rather pleased than otherwise by my speculations, 'I suppose it wouldn't be Veriny Crighton-Jones, by any chance?'

'Right first time, old boy,' Gerald answered, still with the same purring intonation; and I could imagine the self-satisfied grin which overspread his face as he spoke. 'Gosh,' he went on, obviously quite unable to bottle up his feelings any longer, 'gosh, she's a grand girl. . . . I've been seeing quite a bit of her, as it happens. To tell you the truth, I believe she's taken quite a fancy to me. Isn't it extraordinary?'

'Most,' I agreed.

'Well, I mean, I'm a pretty ordinary sort of bloke, and she's —well, she's a bit above my head, to tell you the truth— awfully sophisticated, and all that.'

'Bristling with sophistication, I should think.'

'*Exactly*. Of course, she's frightfully gay, and likes having a good time, but she's really awfully *innocent*, in a way.'

'She never struck me like that,' I said.

'Oh, but you don't know her as well as I—I mean, after all—' Gerald sounded suddenly embarrassed.

'I've known her for five years, on and off,' I said patiently.

'Yes, but what I mean *is*—the extraordinary thing is that Veriny's not like the rest of these good-time girls. She's *different*.'

'That's always a refreshing quality,' I replied.

'Sarcastic old bugger, aren't you?' Gerald retorted. 'Well, Abyssinia—I'll be giving you a ring next week, I shouldn't wonder.'

Gerald duly rang me up, and I could guess, from his voice, that he was still full of his new conquest, and longing to talk about it. We met in the pub at Lambeth; he was there before me and for a second or two, when I entered the bar, I hardly recognized him. Seldom, indeed, before or since, have I seen anybody so much changed in so short a time: Gerald had plainly lost weight, his face, beneath his tan, was paler than usual, and his eyes had an unaccustomed, a positively febrile brightness. One might have supposed him to be sickening of some fell disease, had it not been for the air of bubbling, uncontrollable happiness which he exhaled.

I was careful not to bring up the topic of Veriny, knowing perfectly well that he would be quite unable to keep off it for more than two minutes. Nor was I mistaken: no sooner had we ordered our drinks, than Gerald was launched upon an exhaustive (and to me somewhat exhausting) catalogue of Veriny's charms. Gerald had never been particularly reticent about his sexual life, and was willing enough, usually, to furnish any amount of clinical details about the progress of his affairs. Now, however, I noticed a difference: gone was the crude, medical student's approach, no longer did he refer to the loved one in such terms as he had been wont to employ, in the past, when describing such charmers as Kathleen and Gladys at the Clarendon. His praise was all for the beauty of Veriny's character: her essential simplicity, her capacity for hard work, her generosity ('She actually wanted to pay for dinner—you don't find many girls like that nowadays'). Above all, he extolled her 'difference' from other girls.

'It's wonderful, really, when you think of her being mixed up with all that beastly theatrical set. . . . Most girls wouldn't have been able to stand the pace: it takes a real thoroughbred like Veriny to keep straight in that sort of set-up.'

I listened, with a kind of rueful amusement, to Gerald's ravings. I was tempted, at times, to laugh outright; at the same time, I felt genuinely concerned about him, for this, quite obviously, was no passing *béguin*, but—as Gerald himself never tired of assuring me—the 'real thing'. I rather prided myself, in those days, on being unshockable, and liked to think that no sexual vagary on the part of my friends could surprise me; but I was both astonished and distressed that Gerald—so level-headed, so commonsensical, so mature in his judgment—could be so utterly bamboozled. I was tempted to say outright what I knew to be true: that the only respect in which Veriny Crighton-Jones could be considered 'different' from other girls was in being more drunken, more lascivious and (to do her justice) more beautiful than most. If I refrained from speaking, it was chiefly from a natural reluctance to spoil Gerald's present happiness; it was, moreover, pretty obvious that no warning from me (or anybody else) would have the slightest effect upon him in his present besotted state. Perhaps, too, I was further restrained by a certain distrust of my own motives: the envy and frustration which I was wont to feel on such occasions could too easily (as I knew from past experience) add a sadistic relish to the most well-meant and high-minded of homilies.

Presently the flood of Gerald's eloquence began to subside, and I caught him looking at me with a shy, sidelong glance, as though he were trying to nerve himself to raise some less agreeable and perhaps embarrassing topic.

'By the way,' he managed to stammer out at last, 'd'you happen to know a chap called Bertie Westmacott?'

I said I knew Bertie fairly well.

'Well, the fact is, you see, that he's rather a friend of Veriny's. . . . I haven't met him myself, mind you, but it seems that he and Veriny used to go around together rather a lot, and he still keeps ringing her up about twice a day, and —well, you know, I just wondered what sort of bloke he was.' Gerald paused a moment, then added, forcefully: 'Mind you, I'm not suggesting for a minute that Veriny—I mean, there couldn't really be anything of *that* sort, Veriny's not that kind of girl—but by God, if that chap's been pestering her, I'll have the bloody hide off him.'

As it happened, I was fairly well-informed about Veriny's relations with Bertie Westmacott, and had every reason to suppose that they were wholly innocent, since Bertie's love-life, from all accounts, was almost exclusively bound up with His Majesty's Brigade of Guards. It didn't, however, seem altogether prudent to tell Gerald this, and I consoled him, as best I could, by saying that Bertie was an old friend of Veriny's from her R.A.D.A. days; nor did I add (as I might well have done) that Gerald's threat to 'have the hide off him' would without a doubt have provided Bertie with the thrill of his life. It was perhaps as well (I reflected) that Gerald's jealousy had attached itself to so innocent an object; and I couldn't help suspecting that Veriny herself had been 'playing up' Bertie, quite deliberately, in order to throw Gerald off the scent of other and more blameworthy victims.

Shortly after this I was taken ill, and spent some months in the country; I didn't see or hear from Gerald again till my return to London, when I rang him up and suggested a meeting. We met, once again, in the Lambeth pub, for which we had both developed a fondness. Gerald greeted me genially enough, but I noticed at once that he was looking tired and rather worried, and that he had grown even thinner since our last encounter. For almost the first time since I had known him his geniality struck me as forced: there was a look of strain and, it seemed to me, concealed unhappiness behind the façade of conviviality. Once again I refrained from mentioning Veriny, and on this occasion it was some time before Gerald himself broached the subject.

'By the way,' he said at last, with a curious, rather rueful smile, quite unlike his usual candid grin, 'by the way, I suppose you ought to congratulate me.'

'Congratulate you?' I repeated, mechanically, with a vague, premonitory unease.

'Yes—I thought perhaps you'd have seen it in *The Times*. Veriny and I are being married next month.'

I gaped at him, idiotically, then, with a sudden and complete loss of control, burst out laughing.

'You don't *really* mean,' I gasped, incredulously, trying in vain to stifle my laughter, 'that you and Veriny are actually engaged to be *married*?'

'Yes, that's the idea—I popped the question a couple of months ago. We'd have been married by now, only Veriny didn't want to break her contract. She's in that Charlot show at the Vaudeville, you know—quite a decent little part—you ought to go and see it, if you haven't been. . . . Of course, she'll give up the stage when we're married—she didn't want to, but I put my foot down for once.'

As he spoke, Gerald's face had a curious expression which I had never seen there before: a kind of shy, animal defensiveness, the look of a normally good-tempered dog who has been ill-treated, and has learnt to distrust its owner. I knew (whatever might have happened between him and Veriny) that he was unhappy; and I felt deeply sorry for him. My ill-timed laughter had obviously distressed him, and I tried my best to make up for it.

'Of course I congratulate you,' I said, feeling my words and tone hopelessly inadequate. 'All the very best, and I hope you'll both be frightfully happy.'

'I hope so too,' said Gerald quietly; and there was something in his voice which implied, beyond any possible doubt, that he didn't expect the hope to be realized.

For the rest of that evening Gerald remained pointedly reticent about his forthcoming marriage; and it was not till I had met and talked to him on several future occasions that I began to have some idea of the sequence of events that had led up to his engagement. As it happened, I chanced to meet Veriny herself at about this time, at a party at which Gerald was not present; and bit by bit I was able to piece together, from one source and another, the not-very-edifying story.

Veriny, it seemed (and this much must be conceded in her favour), had quite genuinely fallen in love with Gerald—or at any rate had had (as she herself would have put it) a more than usually exclusive 'thing' about him. This, it appeared, had coincided rather conveniently with a desire on her part to 'settle down'—though I should have found this hard to credit if I had not elicited (from Bertie Westmacott, as it happened) the rather more cogent fact that Veriny had had one of her periodical 'scares': in other words, she had believed herself pregnant as the result of an affair with a young Guards officer, a close friend of Bertie's. More cogent still, perhaps, was the fact that Veriny, in the early days of their relationship, had acquired a wholly misleading impression of Gerald's financial resources. This had come about in a rather odd way: Gerald had introduced Veriny to his sister (who was still employed at her 'perfectly foul' secretarial job in London), and the two girls, so it seemed, had settled down to a nice cosy chat about Gerald's prospects. Sheila, perhaps dazzled by Veriny's smartness and by her rather deceptive air of luxury, and being, herself, extremely snobbish, had given her prospective sister-in-law to understand that Gerald would inherit an extremely comfortable little income. Not content with this, she had apparently implied—though without positively committing herself—that Gerald's father was a regular soldier, a scion of a minor but highly respectable county family, and the owner of a 'place' in Surrey which (it might be supposed from Sheila's description) he had inherited from distant— and even more distinguished—forebears.

It was, so I gathered, on the day following this conversation that Veriny had finally agreed to become engaged to Gerald. Shortly afterwards—at her own instigation, I inferred, rather than Gerald's—she spent a weekend with the Brockhursts at Woking; this had occurred shortly before my own meeting with Gerald, at which he had announced his engagement, and might in itself (as I guessed afterwards) have been quite enough to account for Gerald's defensive and unhappy state of mind on that occasion. It was soon after this that I myself encountered Veriny, and heard her account of the visit.

'My sweet, it's bliss to see you', she exclaimed, disentangling herself, cocktail glass in hand, from a gaggle of young men among whom I recognized Bertie Westmacott and the Guards officer with whom, till lately, Veriny had been 'walking out'. 'I suppose you've *heard*', she went on, 'about Gerry and me' (I had never heard Gerald called 'Gerry' before). 'He's such a sweetie-pie, and I'm madly happy—he's made me realize, you see, that I was just *made* to be a wife and mother' (here Veriny gave me one of her mischievous Constant Nymph grins). 'As a matter of fact, I was within *inches* of breaking it off only last week—my dear, that *family*! *Nobody* had warned me what I was marrying into—poor Gerry's terribly loyal, of course, and won't hear a *word* against them. Of course, I had met that bitchy sister—Moira, or Sheila, or whatever her ghastly name is—and she'd cracked

98

them up as being stinking rich and ever so county, so you can imagine, my dear, my utter *horror*! That frightful house—like a *morgue*, my dear—and of course, the first thing that happened was that I was set on by that bloody dog of theirs —it bit me in the leg, and I swore like a trooper, which of course didn't exactly help to *endear* me. . . . And the awful daughter said it was "only his fun", and the still more awful mother—a perfect *vampire*—said it was Mortal Mind, and my dear, if you can believe it, started to "demonstrate", there and then—clacking her teeth, and making a sort of cooing noise, like a wood-pigeon. . . . My dear, it was all *too* frightful—except for the old man, who's rather a pet—madly common, of course, but really rather pathetic (my dear, the *way* that woman treats him!) and the brother—back on leave from some ghastly outpost of Empire, *oh* so pukka but rather handsome—I'm not sure I didn't make a tiny bit of a hit, but of course Gerry's *wildly* jealous, and always threatening to horsewhip anyone who comes within ten yards of me, which of course *is* rather bliss, though it does have its comic side, because he's always wanting to beat up the wrong people—I thought he was going to *murder* poor darling Bertie, who's as queer as a coot anyway, and only hangs round me because he's in love with Teddy Boscombe' (Teddy Boscombe was Veriny's guardee), 'and as I'm always telling him, he's wasting his time, because Teddy's practically stopped being queer since he met *me*, bless his little heart.'

5

Not long after this I retired once again into the country, and remained there for nearly two years; I didn't see either Gerald or Veriny during this period, and such news as I had of them was fragmentary and intermittent. I received an invitation to the wedding, but refused it on grounds of ill-health. I was, as it happened, genuinely ill; but I should have preferred, I think, in any case, not to be present at the ceremony. Since his marriage, Gerald had become for me (as one's friends, when they marry, are apt to become) slightly unreal; I thought of him as one thinks of a character in a novel with whose fortunes one has identified oneself, but in whom one loses all but a faint retrospective interest when the book is closed. Insofar as I remained objectively aware of his existence, I was inclined to take an extremely pessimistic view of his future; and the news of him which filtered through to me during the next two years was to justify only too abundantly my gloomy prognostications.

Once or twice I heard from him—brief, awkward but rather touchingly affectionate letters, in which he told me almost nothing which I really wanted to know. Veriny was seldom mentioned, and when her name did occur, it was in a context which gave no clue as to the present state of their relationship. Veriny had gone to a cocktail party, a tea-fight or a charity dance—and so forth; sometimes Gerald referred to her, with a curious impersonality as 'my wife'. . . . One could have inferred anything or nothing from such references; Veriny herself never wrote to me, apart from a letter of thanks for my wedding present; this, however, didn't surprise me, for she had always been a poor correspondent.

Gerald had passed his final examinations shortly before his marriage, and had managed to obtain a junior partnership in a country practice near Edinburgh. Only one feature in his letters to me could have been construed as evidence that all was not well with his marriage: this was the growing frequency with which he complained of lack of money. At the time of his marriage, his father had apparently come up to the scratch, and helped him to buy his share in the practice; but the Brockhursts, as I knew, were far from rich, and indeed (despite Mrs Brockhurst's pious economies) were likely to be even less well-off in the future. Gerald was at present almost wholly dependent upon his job; as for Veriny, she had, so I gathered, only a small allowance—scarcely more than 'pin-money'—from her parents, who had strongly disapproved of the marriage. Knowing Veriny's habits and the standard of living to which she was accustomed, I found it hard to believe that she would settle down even for a week—let alone for a lifetime—to the dim, cheeseparing existence of a penurious country doctor's wife.

Poor Gerald, I thought—he had been well and truly 'caught' —trapped at the outset of his career, like many another promising young man, and doomed to a lifetime of near-failure; slogging away at the job at which, in other circumstances, he might have been a conspicuous success. With anybody else, it wouldn't have surprised me in the least; but Gerald, from the earliest days of our acquaintance, had seemed to me the very last person to suffer such a fate. With his toughness, his integrity of purpose, his basic indifference to the snares which beset the average young man, he had seemed destined for a career of solid if unspectacular achievement; that he should have been so easily—and so fatally—deflected from it, seemed to me a more than usually sadistic gesture on the part of 'whatever brute or blackguard made the world'.

Yet, if I am to be honest, I must confess that, beneath my genuine sorrow at his misfortunes, I was aware of a secret, inadmissible feeling of satisfaction. Doubtless I did possess a nasty streak—I am quite prepared to admit it; but Gerald, after all, had stood for me as the prototype of all those virtues which, since I didn't possess them myself, I was apt to envy —and often to resent—in other people. Much as I had liked and admired him, my feeling for Gerald had never been quite without the grain of malice engendered by my own sense of inferiority; and now Gerald, like many another, had been proved vulnerable, and unworthy of the trust which I had placed in him.

As the months passed, I began to acquire further scraps of information about him. Some of it came from a rather unlikely source: Eric Anquetil, teaching at a prep. school in Scotland, had encountered Gerald by chance in Edinburgh, and had been invited once or twice to his home.

'Your nice Gerald', wrote Eric, 'seems changed beyond recognition—I hardly recognized him when we met in the Caley. He seems to be boozing pretty hard—I can put away a fair amount myself, as you may know, but I couldn't begin to keep up with him. He was very incoherent, and kept talking about someone called Boscombe—do you know him, and ought I to? I couldn't quite make out whether G. liked him very much or hated him like poison—he seemed rather ambivalent about the whole thing. I did rather gather, though, that G.'s horns were beginning to sprout, poor dear. It seems centuries since you and he used to go riding at Oxford, do you remember?'

'The Brockhurst home' (he wrote in another letter) 'I found very embarrassing: Veriny was tight as an owl at tea-time, and G. started nagging at her in front of me. I must say, my sympathies were rather on her side, though I was sorry, too, for poor G. He seems to be getting very tetchy and disgruntled, and kept saying how broke he was—at one moment I actually thought he was going to touch me for a fiver, but fortunately he didn't (I only had five bob on me, anyway).

He's busy enough, it seems—plenty of patients—but Veriny has about as much idea as a chicken of keeping house, and obviously spends all the housekeeping money on the Demon.'

A further letter was even more explicit:

'Poor G.'s antlers are definitely burgeoning: I spent a night in Edinbro' at the Caley (having been offered a lift back in time for prayers the next morning), and Veriny B. was staying the night there too. G. was away at some medical function in Carlisle or somewhere, and V. introduced me to the ambivalent Mr Boscombe at tea-time. I made the obvious assumption, but was very tactful. Afterwards, we all had drinks in V.'s bedroom—champagne, I may say. (The wicked Mr B., by the way, is rather an Adonis, and I should guess crypto-musical—he seems to have been a great buddy of Hew Dallas at Oxford.) I got back very late from Francis's party (or rather very early—I had practically no sleep) and as I stumbled upstairs saw him (Mr B.) coming out of V.'s room. I'm sorry for poor Gerald—I give that marriage about another year at most.'

It was from Bertie Westmacott, nearly two years after Gerald's marriage, that I finally heard the news which, in the light of Eric's information, I had been expecting for some time: Gerald was getting a divorce—or rather, was allowing Veriny to divorce him.

'It's all madly complicated, as a matter of fact,' Bertie went on. 'You see, Gerald's known all about Teddy for ages, and was quite prepared to be the *mari complaisant* so long as they were reasonably tactful—in fact, Gerald must have found it quite convenient, seeing that he had such a thing about Teddy himself.'

'*Gerald* had?' I exclaimed, incredulously.

'My dear, it was common knowledge: they were terrific buddies—they went off fishing together one weekend, while *I* stayed with Veriny, and had the time of their lives. I must say, it came as a surprise to *me* when I first realized—I always thought Gerald was madly B.M. before he married, but *there* you are, dear, even an old bitch like me can make a bloomer sometimes.'

'What utter nonsense,' I exploded at last, 'I don't believe a word of it. Why, Gerald was no more like that than—than the Archbishop of Canterbury.'

Bertie's eyes widened.

'My dear, what do *you* know about the Archbishop? Anyway, as I was saying, it might have worked out all right—a sort of *ménage a trois*, you know—if only Veriny had stuck to Teddy, but knowing Veriny, what could you expect? You know how madly indiscreet she is. . . . She was having a great walk-out with a Major in the Black Watch for quite a time —I don't think Gerald knew about it, though he may have had his suspicions. Well, Teddy knew this Major, *and*, my dear, one night Veriny asked them *both* back to dinner. Gerald was called out during the evening, to one of his gruesome patients, and they thought he'd be ages, because it was a rather sticky maternity case, apparently, but it turned out to be a false alarm, and Gerald was back in half-an-hour, my dear, and found all three of them in bed together. . . . Well I do *rather* see Gerald's point, don't you? Cuckolded fore and aft, so to speak, and by the *Black Watch*, my dear. . . . And after all, three in a bed *is* a bit of a crowd, and it *was* Gerald's bed, anyway. But *oh*—'and here Bertie drew a long sigh and raised his eyes to the ceiling—'but oh, my dear, *isn't* our little Veriny a lucky girl?'

Soon after this encounter, I had a letter from Gerald—a brief, pathetic note, giving me the bare facts, and without any of the details (mostly apocryphal, as I preferred to believe) provided by Bertie Westmacott. 'I should like to see you,' the letter concluded. 'Will you be in Town next Wednesday? I shall be up, arranging about the divorce.'

I was staying down at Sandgate at the time—it was in the summer—and the letter had been forwarded from my London address; it was too late now to meet Gerald on the day he had suggested. I wrote to him—an awkward, unsatisfactory letter, in which my expressions of sympathy sounded absurdly pompous and stilted. I had scarcely posted it when Gerald himself walked into my room: he had tried to get me at my home, had heard I was at Sandgate, and had motored straight down the same day.

As Eric had said, he was barely recognizable: haggard, pale, and with a curiously seedy air about him, as though he had slept in his clothes. He came into the room breathing fast, and sat down heavily in an armchair, like a runner at the finish of a race.

'I had to see you,' he said, with a blurred, guttural intonation. At first I thought he had a cold; then I realized that he was drunk.

'Got anything to drink in the house?' he asked, with a shadow of his old, mischievous grin.

'I'm afraid I've only got a bottle of claret,' I said.

'That'll do. I can't talk till I've got a drink inside me.'

I brought the bottle of claret and a tumbler; Gerald poured out the wine impatiently, and took a long drink.

'That's better,' he said. 'Did you get my letter? Oh, you did—so you know what's up.' He paused, then threw his hands apart in a helpless, despairing gesture. 'You see,' he went on, in a flat expressionless tone, 'I'm finished—it's the bloody end of everything, as far as I'm concerned. I'm broke to the wide, for one thing—the practice has gone down the drain, and the divorce is going to cost a fortune, one way and another. I just don't know which way to turn—my people won't do a thing—they wouldn't even if they could, and they can't, anyway; the pater's lost a packet lately. . . . I'm just about sunk, and that's a fact.'

Gerald poured out more claret, and drank down half a tumblerful at a gulp.

'You must wonder why I blew in on you,' he went on. 'I don't want to bore people with my troubles, but I had to see somebody, and—oh well, I don't know: you seem to be the person I've known longest, really, and I've always been rather fond of you, you know. . . . I hope you don't mind—I feel a pretty thoroughgoing bastard at the moment, and I'm being a crashing bore.'

'Of course you're not,' I assured him. 'I only wish I could do something: I suppose there *isn't* anything I could do, is there?'

'Not a thing, thanks all the same: I'm in the shit, and I've just got to grin and bear it, I suppose.'

'Have some more claret,' I said.

Gerald laughed shortly.

'That's a sound suggestion, anyway,' he said, and poured out the remainder of the bottle. I was alarmed by his appearance: his eyes had a feverish, almost an insane glint in them, and his hands trembled pathetically as he poured out the wine. It was five o'clock in the afternoon, and I could hardly suggest that he went to bed; yet bed seemed the obvious place for him in his present condition.

I had reckoned, however, without Gerald's basic toughness,

his ability to bounce up again, like a Russian toy, from the nadir of misfortune. The claret seemed suddenly to take effect: a flush overspread his cheeks, and he smiled at me with something of his own geniality.

'Tell you what,' he said, leaning forward with a sudden, purposeful air, 'let's go and have a swim.'

'All right,' I said, 'if you're sure you're not—' I checked myself, and added, lamely: 'if you're not too tired.'

'Tactful as ever,' Gerald retorted with a chuckle. 'It's all right—I've great powers of recuperation, and a swim'll just about set me up for the evening. Then we'll go out and get stinking. . . . Think I could stay the night in this place?'

'I'll ask the landlady,' I said, and went to seek her out in the basement. There was no room vacant, but I could probably get one down the street, in the house of the landlady's sister.

'Oh, I can sleep anywhere,' Gerald said, when I returned with the news. He looked round the bed-sitting room, which possessed a fair-sized double bed. 'Mind if I cuddle up with you? I'd be damned grateful, actually—I've got into the sort of state when I can't stand being alone, especially at night.'

'I don't mind, as long as you don't,' I said, remembering another, far distant occasion when Gerald had asked me to put him up; I had a sudden, disquieting sense of duplication, as though the wheel of time and experience had come full circle.

'No,' said Gerald, glancing at me with a quick, sidelong smile, 'I didn't think you'd mind.'

We went down to the beach. The sun was still high, but a fresh wind had risen, and the sea didn't look particularly inviting; I was recovering, as it happened, from a bad cold, and decided not to bathe myself.

Gerald, already half-undressed, gave me a mocking grin.

'Not coming in, eh? All right, I won't try and force you.
. . . ' He paused, then added, with a slight chuckle: 'You never
would bathe when I asked you to, would you?'

Once again, it was as though Life had wheeled back upon
itself, to that far-off, wintry afternoon in the flooded fields by
Godstow; and I remembered, with a sudden backwash of
emotion, that odd, crucial moment of decision, so heavily
weighted with a sense of Gerald's destiny and of my own. . . .
But that, I thought, was in another country. . . . A cloud
covered the sun, and I began to shiver in the chilly sea wind.

I watched Gerald undress under a breakwater; his nakedness
made him seem curiously vulnerable and rather pathetic. I
noticed that, despite the haggard leanness of his face, his body
was beginning to run to fat: the muscles were less firmly
modelled, the flesh about the nipples had an almost feminine
softness. I watched him run down the beach and plunge into
the grey, muddy breakers: he swam out a long way, and I
began to feel uneasy. In his present state he was likely to do
something reckless: the sea was rough, and I knew that the
currents could be dangerous. I ought to have warned him. . . .
I remembered his look of blank, unutterable misery as he
spoke of his misfortunes; and the thought struck me, with a
desolating horror, that he might, in a moment of sudden
despair, cease to struggle with the strong, downward pull of
the waves. . . . But I had reckoned, once again, without
Gerald's indomitable toughness and resilience. Soon I saw
him swimming back; and in another three minutes he was
standing by my side, rubbing his chilled body with a towel,
and looking remarkably fresh and revivified after his bathe.

We drank some beers at a pub, and later dined at the Royal
Kent Hotel. Astonishingly, Gerald seemed to have regained
his normal poise almost completely: at dinner he was positively

gay—laughing at old suddenly-remembered jokes from our shared past, and asking for news of people we used to know. It was only afterwards, when we returned to my room (with a bottle of whisky purchased by Gerald), that his mood of spurious, forced geniality seemed suddenly to leave him. He slumped down into the armchair, and for several minutes—while I uncorked and poured out the whisky—he brooded in silence. Suddenly he glanced across at me with a look of temporarily revived alertness.

'D'you know Teddy Boscombe?' he asked.

'Hardly at all,' I said, avoiding his eyes. 'I've met him at one or two parties.'

'Oh, I see—I just wondered,' he murmured vaguely, and lapsed again into silence. For a moment or two he closed his eyes, and I thought he had gone to sleep; presently, however, he began to talk again—haltingly and with many circumlocutions, running his words together, and stumbling over the consonants.

'Bloody done for, that's what I am. . . . Properly scuppered. I don't blame Veriny, mind you—not her fault, poor bitch. . . . It's just the way life bloody well treats people. . . . D'you believe in God?'

'No, I'm afraid not.'

'Nor do I—never was much of a one for religion. . . . I never wanted much for myself, y'know—I wasn't ambitious, like some of these go-getting bastards. . . . I wasn't good enough for Veriny, that's the trouble—no money, no bloody prospects. . . . Know what I'm goin' to do?' He darted the question at me suddenly.

'No, what?'

Gerald grinned at me rather sheepishly.

'You wouldn't guess. . . . The bloody practice's down the

drain—got to sell out. No more private practice for me. . . . Only one thing to do now. . . . '

His voice tailed off, as though he had once again lost interest in what he was saying.

'What do you think of doing?' I asked, as casually as I could.

He looked up at me, as if surprised, then suddenly burst out laughing.

'Why, I'm going for a soldier,' he said.

'D'you mean enlist in the ranks?' I asked, bewildered.

'No, Medical Corps—Rob-all-my-comrades, jolly old poultice-wallahs an' all that. 'Spect I can wangle some sort of commission—not a bad life, and it looks as if things are blowing up for a scrap, with this fellow Hitler and all. . . . I'd rather fancy myself in uniform.'

'It seems a pretty good idea,' I said, cautiously.

'Might get sent abroad, y'know—India, Egypt. . . . Suit me all ri'—fed up with this rotten country. . . . Too small. . . . Wide open spaces—that's the stuff to give the bloody troops. . . . Wait till you see me in uniform. . . . '

He rambled on, more and more incoherently: mostly about the R.A.M.C. and the prospects it offered, but reverting, now and again, with apparent inconsequence, to his divorce.

'S'pose I'll have to go for a weekend to Brighton—that'll be nice, won't it? Might take old Kathleen from the Clarry —wonder if she's still around. . . . Good value, Kathy was. . . . ' He broke off, and gave me a curiously sly, almost shifty look. 'Funny you didn't know Teddy Boscombe,' he went on. 'Thought everyone knew Teddy. Decent sort of chap. . . . Sort of friend I always wanted. . . . I was damned fond of him—used to go fishing together. . . . ' Gerald paused again, eyeing me speculatively. Suddenly he turned his eyes away. 'You didn't know I was like that, did you?' he queried.

'No, I suppose I didn't.'

'Always a bit that way, I s'pose, an' didn't know it. . . . Remember that night at Oxford, when you passed out at the House? Last I saw of you. . . . Chap called Dallas was there —asked me back to his digs. . . . Stayed the night—all rather sordid, really. Hew had a photo of Teddy—told me all about him. . . . Teddy was only half-queer. . . . Liked women too, you know—sort of ambidexterous. . . . Fancied me, though —went fishing together. . . . Funny the way things turn out. . . . '

Gerald's voice petered out into an inaudible mumble: I could see that he was already nearly asleep. I looked at him sadly: so Bertie, I thought, had been right after all; yet the fact refused to lodge itself in my consciousness, my mind rejected it as the queasy stomach rejects a bitter draught.

I roused Gerald at last, and suggested bed. His hand reached automatically for the whisky.

'I shouldn't have any more,' I said. 'Time you went to bed.' I had decided to put him in my bed and sleep in the armchair myself.

'Go and get f——ed,' Gerald retorted, grinning up at me drunkenly but with a sudden, surprising alertness. He poured out half a tumblerful of whisky, drank it off, and rose from his chair: to my astonishment, he seemed perfectly steady on his feet.

'Must go and see about the car,' he said. 'Got some things in the back—toothbrush, razor. . . . '

'I should wait till the morning.'

'No, must go and get toothbrush—always clean teeth at night. . . . You go to bed, ol' boy.'

I offered to go with him, but he seemed determined, for some reason, to go by himself. The car was parked outside, so he couldn't, I thought, come to much harm. I saw him out of the front-door, and returned to my room, where I undressed. Gerald, I thought, seemed an unconscionable long time finding his toothbrush. . . . Anxious not to seem fussy and interfering, I waited for ten minutes; then, in my pyjamas and dressing-gown, went to the front-door and quietly opened it.

Gerald was standing on the other side of the road, beneath a street-lamp, deep in conversation with a private soldier. Hearing the click of the latch, he turned and saw me standing in the doorway. I watched him speak a final word to his companion, then turn and cross the road; he walked steadily enough, though with a certain stiff deliberation. I noticed that the soldier—a tough, rather good-looking young man —continued to stand on the opposite pavement, as though waiting for somebody.

'Sorry, ol' boy—just stayed out to have a breather.' Gerald pushed past me into my room, which was on the ground-floor. As I followed him in, he turned and faced me, with the same sly, evasive expression which I had noticed earlier.

'Look here, ol' boy, if you don't mind frightfully, I think I'll push straight off tonight. . . . Fact is, I ought really to be in Town at ten o'clock tomorrow, and it'll only hold things up if I'm not there.'

'I shouldn't go tonight if I were you,' I said, speaking with an unconcern which I was far from feeling. 'You must be tired after this afternoon, and it's one o'clock already. I'll see we're called early in the morning.'

I saw a flash of irritation cross Gerald's face.

'No, honestly, old boy, I'd rather get off if you don't mind.' His voice was suddenly sharp with impatience.

'But look here,' I said, deciding to risk his anger, 'it's

absolute madness to drive after all that booze—nobody could. You'd much better stay.'

I saw his eyes blaze with anger: yet I was determined that he shouldn't go if I could prevent him, and I remained where I was, standing with my back to the door.

'Look here,' he said, mastering his temper with some difficulty, 'for God's sake don't argue. I know you mean well, but I'm in that sort of state I just can't stand it. And anyway, I'm used to driving when I'm pissed-up—it's become rather a habit with me, lately. I've never had a smash yet—drunkard's luck, I suppose.'

'I'd rather you didn't go, all the same,' I said firmly.

For a moment I thought he was going to lose his temper and become violent: I saw him clench his hands, and his eyes were suddenly blank with rage.

'Oh for *Christ's* sake,' he muttered thickly. A moment later the spasm passed: his face relaxed, and he stared past me, evasively, at the door.

'Sorry, but I'm going. . . . Fact is,' he added, with a carefully assumed casualness, 'I promised that soldier-bloke a lift up to the camp—it's all on my way, you see.'

He took a step forward, and suddenly seized me by both arms. The next moment, I was being half-pushed, half-carried across the room: for a drunken man, the action was performed with a remarkable power and dexterity. Gerald deposited me gently, as though I were an invalid, upon my bed: for a moment he leaned over me, his hands still firmly pinioning my arms.

'Sorry, old chap, but I'm afraid it's goodbye. . . . I know I'm a rotten bastard, but try not to think too badly of me. . . . And take care of yourself.'

A moment later, he was gone. I heard the front-door gently

shut, and the noise of his footsteps, uncannily loud, as he walked towards the waiting soldier and the car.

Gerald's divorce went through with the usual interminable delays; meeting Bertie Westmacott shortly afterwards, I learned that he had applied successfully for a commission in the R.A.M.C., and was at present stationed at Catterick.

'I hear he's become a reformed character,' said Bertie. 'Strictly T.T., and quite drearily respectable—one asks oneself how long *that's* going to last. . . . A friend of mine in the Brigade ran across him, and told me he was going bald and developing quite a paunch. Such a shame—Gerald was never really my tea, but I could see what people *meant* about him.'

Six months after the decree had been made absolute, I saw in *The Times* the announcement of Veriny's engagement to the Hon. Edward Boscombe, of the Coldstream Guards.

In 1937 I received a letter, in a thin and much-smudged envelope, from Sierra Leone. To my astonishment, it proved to be from Gerald. It was so long since I had heard of him, that I half believed him dead, and his letter gave me a curious and not altogether pleasant shock.

'I've done a year out here, and have another year to do,' he wrote. 'It's a good place for the likes of me, and I manage to get quite a lot of fun.' The rest of the letter was taken up with rather dull details about native customs, hunting trips, etc. Enclosed was a photograph of himself, stripped to the waist, and looking comically like an Empire-builder in a tobacco advertisement.

I answered his letter, but he didn't write again, and I heard no more of him for over a year. Then, at Munich time, he suddenly rang me up at my home at Blackheath, and asked me to dinner at his club. At first I didn't catch his name, and the voice seemed wholly unfamiliar—a clipped, military accent which I should never have recognized as Gerald's. My first impulse was to avoid a meeting with him; our last farewell at Sandgate had seemed in some way final: it was as though the real Gerald—the Gerald I had known at Oxford —were dead, and the idea of meeting him again filled me with a curious, almost superstitious dread. Gerald, however, was insistent, and I duly met him, on the appointed evening, at the United Service Club.

His appearance, at least, as he bounced out of the smoking-room to meet me, was reassuring: he was tanned a dark brown, and looked alarmingly fit. I noticed, however, that his hair had receded a good deal, and was going grey at the sides. He greeted me with a rumbustious heartiness, and pushed me before him into the smoking-room. Drinks appeared—sherry for myself, a double gin for Gerald.

'Jolly good luck,' he exclaimed, raising his glass. 'It's grand to see you again. I'm only in Town for a day or two—thought I must look you up. I'll be buzzing down to Netley soon— great hoo-ha going on since this Munich business—matter of fact, I'm sweating on a rather good job—ought to be a bloody Major soon, if I'm lucky—been fart-arsing around with the war-house this last week—can't get a word of sense out of 'em—but here's hoping.'

Gerald drank to his own future, and ordered another round. I felt, suddenly, very ill-at-ease, and wished I had refused the invitation: there was something, it seemed to me, subtly and indefinably *wrong* about the occasion; I had the sense of some evil lurking, like a bad smell, among the solid, conventional trappings of the room. I looked at Gerald again, rather more closely: outwardly, he looked as fit as at any time since I had known him—if anything, fitter; yet, as I studied his face, it dawned upon me, suddenly and frighteningly, that he was a sick man. His nervous, staccato speech, his abrupt movements, a certain strained alertness in his whole manner, seemed somehow to give the lie to his air of bodily fitness.

During dinner, he continued his diffuse, self-centred monologue; only once or twice did he break off to enquire, briefly and perfunctorily, after my own doings. I began to suspect that the occasion was proving as much of a strain for Gerald as it was for myself; it was as though the spate of small-talk and reminiscence (so wholly uncharacteristic of Gerald as I remembered him) were a kind of defence-mechanism, like the ink-cloud secreted by the cuttlefish.

After dinner, in a corner of the smoking-room, Gerald produced from his note-case a bundle of photographs, mostly taken in Freetown. A few of them were of his brother officers, but most were of negroes; some were extremely indecent. I saw that one of the prints, unnoticed by Gerald, had fallen to the floor, and I bent down to pick it up; as I handed it to him, I caught a glimpse of a stalwart young man in bathing shorts, and recognized the face as that of Teddy Boscombe.

As the evening wore on, I became more and more depressed; I tried to appear interested in Gerald's talk, but I realized, sadly, that he had become—quite apart from anything else— a bore. I was thankful when I could at last, with a minimum of discourtesy, make my escape; and I felt pretty sure that Gerald was thankful too.

I had decided that I didn't want to see Gerald again: our long, equivocal and curiously inconclusive friendship seemed to have come to an end at last. Yet Gerald seemed destined to turn up in my life, like some wandering comet, whether I liked it or not. My next and—as it happened—penultimate meeting with him was a year later, during the first weeks of the war. On a flying visit to London, I ran into him in Whitehall, and we had a drink together. The drink led to a beery evening: it was, for Gerald, in the nature of a farewell party, for he was shortly to be drafted to the B.E.F., and seemed extremely pleased about it. He had changed, again, in the past year—this time, I thought, for the better; his nervous self-absorption was less marked, he seemed to have regained some of his old, confident bearing, and, in the nostalgic, war-time atmosphere, so poignant with its perpetual, unuttered sense of last farewells, I felt, in spite of myself, a faint recrudescence of my old affection for him.

'Soon be hanging out my washing on the Siegfried line,' he exclaimed breezily.

It was the sort of remark which, from anybody else, would have exacerbated me, but which, coming from Gerald, I accepted with the tolerance born of long habit. He was wearing the uniform of a Captain in the R.A.M.C., and, as he had predicted, obviously 'fancied himself' in it (he hadn't, it seemed, been able to wangle his majority, as he had hoped a year ago). In my civilian clothes, with a gas-mask slung on a piece of string over my shoulder, I realized that Gerald could still make me feel dim and inferior.

'I shouldn't wonder if it was over by Christmas,' said Gerald (it was the sort of remark that people like Gerald were fond of making at that time). 'By the bye, did you know Teddy Boscombe's been drafted? Oh yes, he went off a week ago—we had a farewell night together. He's probably having the time of his life in Gay Paree by this time. . . . ' Gerald paused, gave a sudden laugh, and added: 'He always did manage to work a flanker on poor muggins.'

It was Gerald's sole reference to the past during the whole course of the evening, apart from a few scraps of news about his own family (his father had died, his mother was living in a hotel in Devon, Sheila was in the A.T.S.). We drank a good deal of beer, and finished up at one of Gerald's 'low dives' in Soho, where I finally left him in the company of a dubious-looking character to whom, it appeared, he had 'taken a fancy'. Our farewells, when it came to the point, were hurried and perfunctory—'Cheerioh, ol' boy, see you in Berlin'— and I wouldn't, in the circumstances, have had it otherwise. Yet I realized, rather to my surprise, after I had left him and was walking home, that I should be genuinely sorry if Gerald were killed. It was the first time that I had consciously felt like this about anybody, and it seemed to me that the war, which up till now had existed, so to speak, only on paper, was beginning at last to be less 'phoney' and more actual.

6

Three years later I was drafted to the Middle-East. I had heard almost nothing of Gerald and very little of anybody else during this period. Occasionally I would hear snippets of news about people I had known from Eric Anquetil, who was employed at the Air Ministry. So-and-so was dead, so-and-so was at the Min. of Inf.; Gerald Brockhurst, it appeared, was somewhere in the Middle-East, but Eric didn't know where. Teddy Boscombe had been killed at Dunkirk, and had apparently left a more than adequate provision for his widow.

'Veriny', Eric wrote, 'seems to be having a pretty good war —I met her at a cocktail-party, surrounded by blond Adonises, and tight as a drum. She has some vague and not too exacting job with E.N.S.A.—"entertaining the troops" (mostly officers, if I know Veriny). She hardly seemed to be pining for the naughty Mr Boscombe, or for poor G. either, for that matter. There's something, I find, peculiarly refreshing about a thoroughgoing and perfectly uninhibited bitch, don't you agree?'

In the summer of 1943 I was stationed at Barce, in the green belt of Cyrenaica, whence I managed to get a week's leave to Alexandria; when I returned, I found that my unit had moved up westwards into the 'blue'. Probably, said the R.S.M. of the hospital to which we had been attached, probably it was Tripoli—but he couldn't be sure. . . . The next fortnight was spent in a prolonged and rather Kafkaesque hitchhike across the Western Desert: it seemed highly improbable that I should ever reach Tripoli, or that my unit would be there if I did. Nevertheless I managed, in due course, to arrive at my destination, where I was absorbed into an enormous and overcrowded transit-camp. It was just after the Sicily landings, and the camp was in a state of chaos: the intakes during the previous week had been prodigious, and nobody seemed to have the faintest idea what anyone was supposed to do, or—which was more important—where anyone was supposed to go.

I was given a job in the cook-house. The day after my arrival a case of smallpox was reported in the town, and all new intakes were ordered to report immediately to the M.I. Room for vaccination. It was useless to protest that I had been vaccinated only a fortnight before: the M.O. simply refused to listen; so I was duly vaccinated all over again, for the second time in three weeks. Following the smallpox scare, came a craze for F.F.I.s. No less than three times, during my stay in the camp, was I forced to parade before an M.O., stark naked, in order to reassure him that I was not suffering from lice, scabies, gonorrhoea or syphilis. The last of these supererogatory inspections was carried out in particularly uncomfortable conditions; the day was exceptionally hot, a new draft had just arrived, and the M.I. tent, when I reached it, was already crowded with upwards of two-hundred naked, sweating soldiers.

For the benefit of those who have not experienced it, it should be explained that the procedure at an F.F.I. is as follows: other ranks queue up, stripped to the waist, and are examined, one by one (though in most cases rather cursorily) by the M.O. As your name is called, you step smartly forward to where the M.O. is sitting, drop your slacks, and raise your arms above your head as though offering a prayer to the sun (the purpose of this oddly hieratic gesture being, in fact, merely to enable the M.O. to make sure you haven't got crabs under the arm-pits).

I duly queued up; I was becoming accustomed, by now, to this particular form of exhibitionism. The tent was very hot, and I was a long way down the queue; the M.O., however, was plainly wasting no time over the job, and the long straggling line of men moved forward with more than usual rapidity. My turn came sooner than I had expected: I took two steps forward, beyond the flap which screened the M.O.'s table, dropped my trousers down to the ankle, and, like a priest officiating at some pre-Christian rite, raised my arms above my head.

For a moment I noticed nothing; then, glancing with the mildest curiosity at the top of the M.O.'s head, I was struck by something oddly familiar about it. The set of the hair, the particular way the ears projected from the sides of the head —surely this was somebody I had known before, years ago, before the war.... The M.O. scrutinized conscientiously (though briefly) my pubic hair; then raised his face to the level of my arm-pits. As he did so, our glances met; and I found myself gazing into the eyes of Gerald Brockhurst.

For a moment we stared at one another as if spell-bound; my own surprise was reflected, comically, in the face of Gerald: his mouth fell open, his eyes bulged in helpless astonishment. Suddenly he leaned back in his chair, dropped his arms to his sides, and exclaimed, in a voice which sounded curiously exacerbated, almost angry:

'What the bloody hell are *you* doing here?'

I looked at the lined, weary face: Gerald had grown much thinner, and his hair was now quite grey; yet he still preserved the timeless, 'thirtyish' air which I remembered, and he looked, I thought, extraordinarily young for his age.

'I—well, I suppose I just happen to be here, sir,' I replied. For an instant, a sense of nightmare descended upon me: the heat was intolerable, and suddenly I began to tremble, afraid that I was going to faint.

'But look here,' Gerald rapped out, in the same exacerbated tone, 'what the hell are you *doing* in this outfit? I mean, it *is* you, isn't it?'

'Oh yes,' I replied, in no particular sort of voice, 'I suppose it's me all right.'

Suddenly Gerald leaned forward.

'Look here, I can't talk to you now,' he muttered (the other ranks behind me were becoming restive, and the medical orderly was casting curious glances at us). 'Stay behind afterwards, d'you mind?'

'Very good, sir,' I replied, stolidly, and, pulling up my trousers, shuffled out of the tent.

Afterwards, when the queue had dispersed, I returned, and

talked to Gerald while the orderly cleaned up the mess in the M.I. Room.

'But look here,' Gerald kept repeating, 'what the hell are you doing as a private, anyway? Surely you could have got a commission of some sort.'

I assured him that I was perfectly happy where I was.

'But dammit, man, it's all nonsense—you ought to be doing something better than this. . . . What *do* you do, anyway?'

I explained that I belonged to a V.D. treatment unit.

'A pox-wallah, eh? My Christ, that beats everything!' Gerald exclaimed, and burst into a violent fit of laughter. As he laughed, his face lost its look of strain and anxiety, and it was the old Gerald who, as his mirth subsided, grinned affectionately at me across the table.

'God, what a bloody awful war this is,' he said; and I noticed that he had suddenly become serious—almost gloomy —again. 'I suppose,' he added quietly, 'you heard about Teddy Boscombe?'

'Yes, I heard he was killed at Dunkirk.'

'It was a damned shame,' Gerald muttered, not looking at me. 'I was fond of Teddy, you know—fonder than I've ever been of anybody, I suppose.' He was silent for a moment, then added, conventionally: 'It's hard luck on Veriny.'

I said nothing: reflecting, sadly, that Teddy's death was not Veriny's tragedy but Gerald's.

'Look here, we must have a chin-wag,' Gerald exclaimed, with sudden briskness. 'The trouble is, though, it's going to be so damned difficult to—I mean, I can't very well ask you round to the mess, and—oh Christ,'—Gerald flung out his arm in a violent, futile gesture—'what a bloody *hopeless* war this is!'

Suddenly he grinned at me, and held out his cigarette-case.

'You were always a bit of a dark horse, weren't you?' he chuckled. 'Tell me, why didn't you try for a commission?'

'I suppose because I didn't particularly want one,' I answered.

'Yes, but—oh, I dunno: you're probably better off in some ways. . . . Being a bloody doctor, I wouldn't have had much choice, anyway. . . . I haven't had much of a war, though. See here, can't I talk to you—properly, I mean? Trouble is, this camp is lousy with bloody officers and provost companies and what not. . . .' Gerald grinned again, with a boyish embarrassment. 'Of course, I know it's all bullshit, but in a place like this—'

'Oh, that's all right,' I said quickly. 'It's just one of those things. . . . Let's meet again after the war—we'll have a date in that pub at Lambeth, where we used to go when you were at Thomas's—d'you remember?'

A happy smile once again overspread Gerald's tired, harrassed countenance.

'All right, we'll do just that: I'll keep you up to it. . . . I'm expecting to be shifted in a day or two, anyway. By Christ, though, it's a lousy war, isn't it?'

'Yes,' I agreed, 'it's a lousy war.'

We were silent for a moment; and I was aware, in the hot, airless tent, of a sudden feeling of aloofness, as though I were gazing down at our two selves from some remote, Olympian height.

Gerald looked at his watch.

'Well, I suppose I must be pushing off,' he said, and I noticed that his voice had taken on an impersonal, faintly 'official' tinge. Taking the hint, I came to attention and saluted.

Gerald grinned as he returned my salute.

'Cheerioh, old boy,' he said, 'be seeing you sometime.'

123

I left the tent and walked through the blinding sunlight towards my own quarters.

I never kept my date with Gerald in the pub at Lambeth.

A year or two after the war, I happened to go into a bar off the Tottenham Court Road with which I had been familiar in the past. The first person I saw, as I entered, was Bertie Westmacott—older and balder, but with an air of perennial (if somewhat spurious) youthfulness.

He offered me a drink. He was working for the British Council, he told me, and expected soon to be sent to Greece —'my spiritual home, definitely, my dear.' He was as full of gossip as ever, but I knew so few of the people to whom he referred, that I found his talk tedious. It occurred to me, suddenly, to ask for news of Gerald, of whom I had heard nothing since our meeting in Tripoli.

Bertie's eyes widened with incredulous astonishment.

'But d'you mean to say you haven't *heard*?'

I explained that I had spent the last few weeks in Italy, and had heard no news of anybody.

'Oh my dear, the most *ghastly* affair—splashed all over the *News of the World*, too squalid for *words*. I always *said* Gerald'd come to a sticky end, and *how* right I was.'

I felt my stomach contract with a sudden queasiness: knowing, before I put my next question, what the answer would be.

'Is he dead?' I asked.

Bertie nodded, his face suddenly grave.

'He got into trouble, you see—in Germany. You can guess what *sort* of trouble. . . . The details all came out—they were pretty shaming, I must say, and *I'm* no prude, I'd have you know. . . . Anyway, he was up for court-martial—under close arrest, and all that—but he must have bribed one of his guards, or something, because he managed to get hold of a service-revolver and blow his brains out. One only hopes that, being a doctor, he made a decent job of it.'

Oddly enough, after that first premonitory spasm, I found that I could feel no genuine emotion whatsoever. I was not really much surprised by the circumstances of Gerald's death, nor did I feel particularly shocked. The Gerald who had died —the ageing, unhappy Army officer—seemed to have so little real connection with the Gerald I had known that I found it all but impossible to connect the two; and the fact that a man bearing the same name had blown out his brains in a prison-cell in Germany, seemed irrelevant and without meaning.

I listened without very much interest as Bertie, with a certain macabre relish, related the details of the case. They were, as he had said, sufficiently squalid, and my curiosity was soon more than satisfied. I interrupted him at last to enquire after Veriny, about whom I had heard almost nothing since before the war.

'But where *can* you have been living?' Bertie exclaimed. 'My dear, she's madly notorious—she married that ghastly steel-millionaire, Vögelkraut, and came over all grand: she won't know *any* of us, nowadays. Stinking with money, of course—but *stinking*. . . . Oh yes, young Veriny's done pretty well for herself—one of the hard-faced women who look as though they'd done well out of the war. Though I must say, filthy lucre *quite* apart, I can't think *how* she puts up with old Vögelkraut—bald as a coot, my dear, with at least half-a-dozen chins, and a simply *enormous* tummy. She used to have rather a pretty taste in husbands, after all. . . . Poor Teddy— I simply wept *gallons* when he was killed. I never *really* took

to Gerald, though—he always seemed to me madly ungay.'
Bertie paused, eyeing me with a mild, reminiscent curiosity.
'You and he were rather buddies, at one time, weren't you?'

'Yes,' I said, 'I suppose, in a way, we were.'

I got away at last, and walked down the Tottenham Court
Road, through the drenching, blustery weather of an English
June; musing, with a remote, unpassionate sadness, upon
Time's revenges and all the ruined years.

Kurt Schlegel

1

KURT SCHLEGEL first came into my life towards the end of 1942: I was serving in the R.A.M.C., in Palestine, and one day he turned up—a new posting to the unit, a Palestinian; or, as one of our N.C.O.s politely put it, 'a f——ing Yehudi'. I came across him wandering about the camp, looking lost and disconsolate, and not a bit like the accepted idea of a British soldier. He was wearing his greatcoat on top of his battledress, and staggered beneath the weight of his full kit and an enormous bundle of bedding; with his big body and rolling gait he reminded me of those old cartoons in *Punch* in which the Russian Bear used to be pictured in the uniform of a Tsarist soldier.

I went up to him and asked if I could help: he grumbled his thanks, and said that he'd just come from the Q stores, and had been told to find an empty bed-space in one of the tents. As it happened, I knew that there was a vacant one in my own tent, so I showed him the way to it. He dropped his blanket roll, and slumped down on it, glaring angrily in front of him, and taking not the slightest notice of myself.

I wasn't, to tell the truth, much attracted to him—he seemed grumpy and rather hostile—yet from the first I was, obscurely, prejudiced in his favour: perhaps for no better reason than that he was a foreigner, and therefore (as I supposed) likely to be more intelligent than the average British private. I was new to the unit myself, and had so far made no friends; the unit—a V.D. Treatment Centre—was in any case a small one, and, like most small units, inclined to be 'cliquey' and exclusive. I felt sorry for this new 'intake', who would probably feel even more of a fish out of water than I did myself; and I decided, there and then, that I would make friends with him.

This, however, proved to be less easy than I had supposed. At dinner-time I sat next to him: his manner was still grumpy and discouraging, and he answered my questions irritably and with evident reluctance. He spoke English fairly fluently but very badly, with a strong German accent; his grammar was terrible, but he made up for this by shooting out his words with an almost truculent self-confidence. I gathered that he was an Austrian, that he had emigrated to Palestine in 1939, and had enlisted in the British Army a few months ago. His name was Kurt Schlegel: he spelt it for me carefully (pronouncing the letters as though they were German—'Ess, tsay, arsh,' etc.), doubtless assuming that I was as illiterate as most of my race. I found myself mildly resenting this; then cursed myself for my own snobbery and class-consciousness.

Even without his greatcoat and his webbing equipment there was still something ponderous and rather clumsy about him, and I continued to think of him as a big, shaggy, ungainly bear. His face was broad and fleshy, typically Jewish-Central-European, with a habitually louring, minatory expression: I was reminded, vaguely, of those bronze busts of Beethoven which people sometimes stand on the tops of their pianos. Once or twice—it was when he was talking about the Nazis —a spark of passionate anger would suddenly flash from his eyes, and he reminded me more than ever of Beethoven: I could imagine him, almost, in the conventional Beethoven posture—standing on some storm-blasted hill-top and shaking his fist at the thunder.

Next day, as it happened, we were detailed for the same job. This consisted of sorting out and arranging under their proper categories an apparently endless hoard of hospital case-cards—Army Form I 1220. I was surprised—for he must, after all, be new to the job—by Kurt's efficiency, though I noticed that he was apt to be impulsive and rather over-confident. We talked, intermittently, while we worked: at one point, the topic of music happened to crop up—I forget how or why—and some remark of mine (I think I had mentioned Debussy) made Kurt glance up at me in wide-eyed astonishment.

'So then, you like the music?' he ejaculated, in the tone of one who discovers that a Fiji islander is able to converse in classical Greek. 'This, I find, is something most strange,' he continued. 'I tell you now something: I am not yet meeting one British boy who has heard of any music but the jazz already.'

Further surprises awaited him: I had heard of—and even read—Verlaine and Baudelaire. More astonishing still, I was familiar with the names of Goethe and Schiller—though I couldn't claim to have read them.

'I think then your parents are perhaps in good position, isn't it?' Kurt wondered, his voice suddenly taking on a less defensive, more intimate tone than hitherto. 'Perhaps you go to the public-school?' he added, cautiously.

I explained that I had been to Bedales, which, though not exactly a public-school, was supposed to be quite a superior institution. Such fine distinctions meant little, however, to

Kurt, who decided thereupon that I had acquired my education at what he insisted upon calling a 'lycée'.

Gradually he began to tell me more about himself: he had studied medicine in Vienna, but had had to give it up for lack of funds; instead, he had qualified as a dental mechanic. Since his emigration to Palestine he had subsisted by a series of menial jobs—working in the orange-groves and being a baker's errand-boy, among others. 'But I do not care,' he would say. 'It is better to be free, even if you have to work like nigger. And now I am soldier in the British Army, because no one can be free till we beat those Nazi bastards, isn't it?'

I began to like Kurt more and more: not merely because he was 'educated', and knew the difference between Debussy and Ravel, but for himself. The rest of the unit, however, didn't share my liking for 'that big fat Yehudi'; nor did poor Kurt improve matters much by his own attitude. I don't think he really meant to be morose or unfriendly: it was mostly shyness, and the fact that he was never allowed to forget that he was a Jew. It is generally supposed that anti-semitism is rare among the British working-class; in fact, it is only too prevalent, especially in the Services, and the isolated Jew—particularly if he is a 'foreigner', like Kurt Schlegel—is apt to find himself cast for the rôle of scapegoat. Kurt was seldom openly insulted—the British soldier's methods are more insidious—but he couldn't fail to notice the muttered comments about 'Yehudis', the music-hall chestnuts about Moses and Ikey-Mo, the Cockney parodies of his accent. Not surprisingly, he remained aloof and rather hostile, scarcely speaking to a soul apart from myself, and often ignoring even my efforts to be friendly.

I did my best, but it wasn't easy to penetrate his tough, defensive carapace. He distrusted and despised the lot of us—myself hardly less than the others—and too often I would find myself repelled and irritated by his racial pride and by his extreme touchiness. More than once he had asked me, in a mood of unaccustomed humility, to 'teach him the good English'; yet if ever I ventured to correct his grammar, he would become irritable and argumentative, insisting that what he said was correct, and implying, with an absurd arrogance, that I didn't know my own language.

'But Kurt,' I protested, on one such occasion, 'we don't say "the card that herein is" '—we were still employed upon the A.F.s I 1220—'we say "the card that's in here." '

'Ach, I do not believe!' he flared out at me, angrily. 'This expression I have seen in English book already, it is correct, I have learnt it in the school.'

'I bet you didn't,' I retorted, stung to sudden annoyance.

'Listen, I tell you now something,' Kurt shouted, his face scarlet with fury, 'when I am student in Vienna I read the English classics in original—Shakespeare, Byron, Galsworthy—and I think I know what is right, what wrong, isn't it?'

'Oh, all right,' I agreed, 'have it your own way,' and immediately changed the subject. It simply wasn't worth quarrelling with Kurt over a mere point of grammar, and I soon gave up my attempts to improve his 'English'; he continued, during all the time I knew him, to speak it with the fluent inaccuracy of a Central-European who knows several languages fairly well but none perfectly.

To say that Kurt was tough would be to put it mildly: he had that illimitable fatalism which is the heritage of his race;

and he was inured to hardship and disaster not only by tradition but by personal experience. His family history was a story of pogroms and endless uprootings; and he himself—from his childhood onwards—had been acutely conscious of being an outcast, a misfit, who could never be finally absorbed into the society which provided the outward framework for his life. His family were strict Jews—his father was a cantor at the synagogue—and uncompromising in their resistance to the growing forces of persecution; Kurt had watched the rise of Hitler, and, in the 'thirties, had become for a time a communist party-member. I don't think his communism went very deep; for him it was primarily a gesture of protest, and a means by which he, as an outcast, could acquire a sense of solidarity with some kind of social group. Also, perhaps, it enabled him to rationalize his hatreds—for Hitler, for Dollfuss, for Franco. He was a great hater; and his hatred had that implacable and profoundly Jewish quality which demands an eye for an eye, a tooth for a tooth. At times I would feel faintly repelled by this aspect of his personality, and once or twice, disturbed by his vengeful diatribes, I ventured mildly to protest.

'Ach, you English, you are *sentimentalisch*,' he would blaze back at me, insolently. 'You do not know what the life is, you live always in the dream. But one day—' and here he would raise his voice and shake his fist at me with the air of some exalted minor prophet—'one day, I think, you wake up, and then you shall see that it is true what I now say.'

Such outbursts as this, however, were comparatively infrequent, and for the most part Kurt remained glumly uncommunicative. His aloofness stood him, often, in good stead: it took a good deal to shake him, and when the rest of us groused at some minor infringement of our liberty—extra fatigues, or a full marching-order parade—Kurt would shrug his shoulders, contemptuously, as though to imply that he thought our complaints petty and childish. It was hardly surprising, after all (I thought), if the small daily miseries of our life seemed to him trivial against the background of his own personal tragedy.

A few weeks after Kurt's arrival we moved up from Palestine to Tobruk, where we were to be attached to a Casualty Clearing Station. It was soon after Alamein, and conditions were chaotic; we arrived at Tobruk to find, as was to be expected, that the C.C.S. had never heard of us. Rations were short, and there was no spare accommodation: we spent the first night in the mortuary tent which happened, by good luck, to be untenanted.

'So then, they think we are dead,' Kurt remarked, with a ponderous irony; then added, after a pause, staring through the tent-flap at the illimitable prospect of barren scrub: 'I think perhaps I would not mind so much, in effect, if I am now dead already.'

The next two days were spent in pitching tents to accommodate ourselves and our medical equipment. In Palestine we had been attached to a cushy unit in a base area; but there was nothing in the least cushy about Tobruk. We worked hard in conditions of extreme discomfort: rations and water were in short supply, sandstorms blew down the tents before we had finished putting them up, the ubiquitous sand invaded our equipment, our food, and the most intimate crannies of our bodies. The unit, till now so 'cliquey' and uncoordinated, acquired a sudden sense of solidarity: I found myself for the first time on friendly terms with people I had scarcely spoken to before; even Kurt, I noticed, had lost some of his aloofness, and, in consequence, began to be accepted, by the rest of the unit, almost as one of themselves.

We stayed at Tobruk just long enough to open up the hospital and to start taking in patients; then a signal came through and we moved up to Barce. Here we were attached to a General Hospital; our billets had been previously occupied by Italian colonial troops, and were infested with bugs. More even than at Tobruk we were thrown back, as a unit, upon our own resources; our quarters were separate from the main hospital, and, as 'pox-wallahs', we found ourselves treated more or less as outcasts. It was no new experience for us; invariably the worst billets and the scrag-ends of any 'amenities' that were going fell to our lot. We were content, however, on the whole, to be thus neglected; for, if the amenities were lacking, so were the more irksome forms of military discipline.

'I tell you now something,' remarked Kurt, with sly satisfaction, 'if we are in comfortable billet at the hospital, then they make us do the fatigue, the fire-picquet, the C.O.'s parade. Here we do f—— all, we are lucky; am I not right?'

We were, in fact, a pretty cushy mob, and there was a tacit understanding between N.C.O.s and privates that we could do very much as we liked, in off-duty hours, provided we kept quiet about it. For all that, there was plenty of grousing —the food was inadequate, duty-hours were arranged unfairly, and so on and so forth.

Such complaints would sometimes rouse Kurt to an outburst of contemptuous anger.

'Listen, my friend,' he would say, 'I tell you now something: you say you do not get enough for the dinner, you do not get your half-day just when you want, you have the bugs in your bed—but in effect you are bloody lucky that you are not in slit-trench up at the front, isn't it?'

At Tobruk, the hostility of the unit towards Kurt had changed to a kind of grudging respect; at Barce he was to become almost popular. His profound fatalism, his cynical acceptance of inevitable misfortune, made our small complaints seem silly and undignified; and it was, I think, this same quality, combined with his toughness and his sense of fair play, which endeared him, at last, even to those of us who had most disliked him. A mean action could provoke him into a thunderous outburst of rage; on the other hand he would (and often did) share his last cigarette or bar of chocolate with the next man—and often with the very same who had called forth his fury a few minutes before.

He suffered, increasingly, from recurrent fits of gloom; and I knew that he was worrying about his mother and father and the rest of his family, whom he had left in Austria in 1939, and of whom he had heard nothing for many months. By now he feared the worst—only too justifiably, as it turned out. Yet an extraordinary natural gaiety came to his rescue; he would switch, with a bewildering rapidity, from the depths of gloom to a mood of sudden, uninhibited cheerfulness:

'Ach, now I would like to dance, to drink some wine, to sing,' he would exclaim. 'I think I go now to the town and see what I find.'

These expeditions into Barce were not, on the whole, very productive—or so I gathered. Once, however, he returned with a bottle of Chianti—a great triumph. When opened, it proved to be rather musty; none the less we enjoyed it—late at night, in one of the treatment-rooms, in the company of two chosen friends.

'Ach,' Kurt exclaimed, leaning back in his chair, and brandishing his half-empty tin mug, 'do you know what I would now like? I would like to be sitting in nice café in a big city—Wien, I think. There I drink my coffee, I read the papers, I watch pass the beautiful girls. Then I eat good dinner with some nice wine, and afterwards I go to good *Konzert*. Then, after this *Konzert*, I find nice girl, and we arrange that we go home to her house, and we make the love—isn't it?'

Then he would break off, heave a deep sigh of nostalgia, and add: 'But here you are, we are just British swaddies, we cannot have nice dinners and beautiful girls. But when this f——ing war is over, then we enjoy ourselves once again, isn't it?'

On one occasion an impromptu sing-song took place in the O.R.s' mess—there had been an issue of beer from the N.A.A.F.I., a rare occurrence at that period. After the old favourites had been droned out, dismally, in chorus—'Nellie Dean', 'Saïda Bint', 'Somewhere in France with you'—Kurt suddenly rose to his feet. The unaccustomed beer—it was Canadian, and rather potent—had gone to his head slightly; his hair was tousled, his eyes had a wild, visionary gleam.

'So then, I now sing,' he announced; and immediately, without an instant's hesitation, burst into a wild, melancholy Magyar folk song. I never knew—though I was to hear it on many subsequent occasions—what the words meant, or even what the song was called; I think it was supposed to be the lament of some peasant girl abandoned by her lover. Kurt's voice was nothing very remarkable—a strong, rather harsh baritone—but he sang now with a yearning, passionate intensity which seemed to embody not only his own personal tragedy but the vaguer, more diffused sadness which afflicted all of us. Listening to those long-drawn, melancholy cadences, we were made suddenly, more acutely aware of our own unhappiness—our profound nostalgia for England, our war-weariness, the whole intolerable burden of our exile.

The effect of the song upon the unit was astonishing: if Kurt had been Miss Vera Lynn or even Bing Crosby himself, he could hardly have been applauded with more enthusiasm. He sang the same song again, and other songs; his glass was filled and refilled with beer; when he was finally allowed to sit down again, I saw that his eyes were bright with unshed tears.

Kurt's real popularity with the unit, dated, I think, from that night. Thenceforward, he began to be regarded not only with tolerance and respect, but with something very like affection. Suddenly, overnight, he had ceased to be an outcast, a mere 'bloody Yehudi', and had acquired the status of a sacred bard, the *Dichter* who, by his inspired utterances, could purge us of our woes.

2

Kurt and I stuck together, by good luck, for the next two and a half years. From Barce we moved up to Tripoli, then to Sicily and Italy, following in the rear of the Eighth Army up to the Adriatic coast.* Both Kurt and I loved Italy—the wine, the food, the people. Sometimes we struck lucky, sometimes not: at Bari we could go to the opera, or have dinner—in mortal fear of red-caps—at out-of-bounds restaurants; elsewhere we were less fortunate; yet the mere fact of being back in Europe, after those long, arid months in the Middle-East,

* I have described elsewhere some of the experiences which befell us during this period.

was a delight which more than compensated, so far as Kurt and I were concerned, for our incidental misfortunes.

Kurt's popularity with the unit persisted; moreover, the M.O.s and N.C.O.s knew him to be conscientious and dependable, with the result that he was liable to be landed with the least popular jobs.

'See now,' he would burst out, angrily, 'that bastard staff-sergeant put me now on nights again—and for vy is this? I tell you: it is because he knows I am conscious in the work, not like these bastards that do not care a f—— about the poor bloody patients. So then, I think now I become not so conscious, I make myself cushy a little, isn't it?'

Yet Kurt remained, despite these occasional flare-ups, as 'conscious' (he could never quite manage the word 'conscientious') as before. His attitude to the patients was remarkable: though only a private, he could, when necessary, instil into them the kind of holy terror usually associated with sergeant-majors. If they didn't turn up punctually for their sulphonamide tablets or their penicillin injections, he would break into one of his violent, annihilating rages; and oddly enough the patients—tough commandoes and guardsmen, many of them—would behave as though he were, in fact, a sergeant-major. Yet Kurt, if he sometimes terrified them, would attend to their wants with a devotion rare among medical orderlies; for all his apparent 'toughness', he was extraordinarily kind-hearted, and at times—if a patient were genuinely ill, for instance—he was capable of an almost feminine tenderness.

In the early autumn of 1944 the unit, which had remained—apart from occasional postings—intact for the last two years, was at last disbanded. Fortunately, Kurt and I were posted together; but the break-up of the unit meant the break-up of a whole way of life to which we had become accustomed; and the prospect of making new friends and of having to adapt ourselves to a new régime weighed heavily upon us.

After several temporary attachments, we found ourselves at last on a hospital ship bound for a coastal town up north— Porto San Marco.* We had had bad reports of it: most of the town was in ruins, the civilians had been evacuated *en masse*, there was no *vino* to be had. Even from the sea, as we drew inshore, the place looked unpromising: a muddle of grey, dead-looking houses clinging to a semi-circle of low hillocks about a narrow bay. Like so many Italian coast towns, it had a precarious air, as though at any moment it might topple into the sea and be submerged.

Squatting on our kits on the troop-deck, we watched the town as it approached us across the heaving water: emerging gradually from the grey, indeterminate blur, taking on definition like a buried memory pushing its way to the surface of the mind. Beyond the town itself we could now see a range of grey, angular hills, their tops half-hidden in the wrack of a retreating storm.

'So then,' Kurt remarked suddenly, echoing my own thoughts, 'now we come to Porto San Marco, now we finish the good times, we are soldiers again, we have all the f——ing bullshit, like bloody rookies.'

'Too true,' I said.

'Is it not strange?' he went on. 'When things are bad, before the Invasion, when we still might lose the war, then we enjoy ourselves, it is like holiday. Now the war is nearly over, they send us to this bastard place, this place in all Italy. . . . Ach! If we could come to Firenze, now, or Rome—then I do not mind the work, I do not mind the bullshit, but here you are,

* This was not the town's real name.

we are soldiers, f——ing *soldati inglesi*, so what you want, hey?'

'I don't want,' I said unhappily. Kurt had a way of luxuriating, masochistically, in our misfortunes; presently, when he had exhausted his capacity for pessimism, he would cheer up, and moan less than anybody. His pessimism was a kind of prophylaxis, a self-inoculation against his own misery. My own depression was less easy to shake off: for some time, now, I had been haunted by a sense of vague, impending disaster. There was not much reason for it—in fact there were a good many reasons against it: the end of the war was in sight— Paris had fallen, Jerry had been driven from one pocket after another, the Russians were advancing every day. My melancholy was just war-weariness, I supposed: with the end in sight, our carefully built-up resistance was beginning to flag. We began to think in weeks instead of years, every small set-back to the Allied Armies seemed an inexcusable postponement of our own release.

'No, you don't want, I don't want,' Kurt was saying, 'but we are in the f——ing British Army still. And I tell you, in effect we are still lucky that we are not in fighting unit, that we are not even in Field Ambulance, isn't it?'

It was true enough; so far we had been extraordinarily lucky—compared with most people we had had a 'good' war; yet I lacked Kurt's ability to count our blessings. The grey, dismal town, backed by the stormy sky, seemed to me at that moment profoundly ominous: a visible and disquieting symbol, not only of our immediate future, but of that remote, unimaginable post-war world to which, since the D-Day landings, we had already begun to look forward.

We docked at last, and were marched off through the ruined streets of the town. The main street leading up from the harbour was called, with a pleasing irony, Via della

Vittoria; there seemed to be red-caps everywhere, but not a single civilian in sight. Over ruined doorways, shop signs still showed pathetically: *Vino, Carne, Parruchiere per Signora*—otiose and without meaning as the *graffiti* at Pompeii. In one shattered window stood a wax model of a little girl, beneath the gilt-lettered inscription: *Al Paradiso dei Bambini*.

'I do not think,' Kurt commented grimly, 'that the *bambini* have much paradise left now, in this horrible town.'

Porto San Marco was to prove quite as unpleasant as we had expected. There was, I think, something inherently evil and corrupt about the town: its streets exhaled an atmosphere of immitigable hostility—a harsh, ungenerous quality such as I had not before encountered in Italy. During the next few months we were overworked, restless and unhappy, waiting despondently for the end of the war; our boredom tempered only by small infrequent pleasures—a sunny day, an afternoon's swimming, an occasional bottle of wine. Both Kurt and I disliked the unit; our Commanding Officer was a fussy, incompetent little man, a country G.P. who had somehow acquired 'specialist' rank as a venereologist, and was totally unfitted for any position of authority; our work was made doubly hard by the atmosphere of hysteria which, like an irritant gas, he generated whenever he appeared. Not surprisingly, he was unpopular, and the unit became increasingly mutinous and uncooperative; only Kurt preserved a seemingly unshakable, a positively monumental calm. I envied him, as always, his limitless fatalism: for myself the small disasters of Army life would always loom more largely, I lacked Kurt's ability to see them, as it were, *sub specie aeternitatis*.

One day, several weeks after our arrival, Kurt and I managed to get an afternoon off together. Just as we were going

out, the Staff-sergeant caught us, and detailed us to go down
to the D.I.D. to collect rations. The whole business was quite
unnecessary: there was plenty of civilian labour to do the job,
and I felt pretty sure that it was a piece of pure spite on the
Staff-sergeant's part. Kurt, as it happened, felt the same:

'The bastard,' he muttered, almost before the Staff was out
of earshot, 'he knows we have half-day, he does not like that
the friends enjoy themselves together, he thinks he will
stop it.'

We had been working for weeks with scarcely a break,
and for several days past had looked forward to those few
hours of freedom; now they were to be taken from us. It
wasn't much, perhaps; a month or two hence we should
already have forgotten the incident. But while it lasted
our misery was overwhelming.

'Ach, never mind,' Kurt said, seeing my woebegone face.
'We will have nice times again. Today that bastard takes away
our little piece of happiness, but he cannot take all.' He paused,
then added, ruminatively: 'It is funny, you know—if a civvy
now would ask you why you are so unhappy and you tell
him, he would laugh at you. You are lucky that you have
nothing worse, he will say. Yet for us it is tragedy, it is like
the death.'

It was quite true, I thought: a civilian would laugh at our
misery. The essential horror of Army life remained always
incommunicable: this piling-up of petty miseries and humi-
liations, so trivial in themselves, into a total of such desolating
catastrophe. The loss of our half-day was nothing in itself:
but coming when it did, on top of all the minor exacerbations
of the last weeks, it seemed, as Kurt said, like a kind of death.

Yet even Kurt could, on occasion, be provoked into

a mood of rebellion. Not long after our abortive half-day, the C.O. took it into his head to confine the entire unit to barracks for some pettifogging offence—somebody, I think, had left his bed-space untidy for the weekly barrack-room inspection. This mass-punishment was grossly unfair, and the unit was already in an ugly mood; yet we had no effective means of redress, and, if it had not been for Kurt, should probably have contented ourselves with abusing the C.O. behind his back. Kurt, however, usually so fatalistic—and so law-abiding—decided, for once, to dig his heels in.

'I think this Major is mad,' he exploded. 'Here we work for weeks like the slaves, and now because some silly bastard does not make proper his bed, this madman confines us to the barracks, he forbid us the exercise and the fresh air that we need. So then, do you know what I now do? I ask interview from the Staff-sergeant and I go to the Major and make complaint.'

Most of us tried to dissuade him—it wouldn't do any good, it might make matters worse. But Kurt was adamant: and the more we argued with him, the more angrily determined he became:

'Ach, you people, you make me sick,' he shouted, his eyes blazing with a prophetic fury, 'always you grouse, you complain, you let shit on your head this bastard Major, and you do f—— all. Listen, then, I tell you something: I am not slave, I am not in concentration camp, and this bastard can go and get stuffed.'

Rather to our surprise, Kurt did ask to see the Major, and was even granted an interview. It didn't do any good; we continued to be confined to barracks; but Kurt had made his protest, and the mere fact of having done so gave him a profound moral satisfaction.

'I do not mind that I do not get what I want,' he declared. 'I have my interview, I make complaint, I do not let shit on my head—that is enough. When I am communist in Austria before the war, I do the same: I make demonstration, I march with banner, I make nuisance. I do not really think, even in that moment, that I help the cause of the workers; I think only that I make protest—I satisfy myself, afterwards I am more happy in my conscience. Do you not think that I am right?'

During the next few months I came to value Kurt's friendship more highly even than before. Since the break-up of our old unit, our relationship had, I suppose, entered upon a more intimate phase; our present comrades were a poor lot, and neither of us, perhaps, found it easy to make new friends. At this time we were almost entirely dependent upon each other's company; and I began to form a clearer idea of Kurt's character. He was, in some respects, highly civilized, yet in others extraordinarily simple, almost a *naïf*. His generosity was unstinting, and, as a friend, he was scrupulously loyal; yet he could on occasion be unreasonable, wrong-headed, even stupid; and at times his Hebraic, eye-for-an-eye conception of justice would lead him into judgments which seemed to me cold-blooded and gratuitously cruel. He would still, for instance, rage against the Nazis, and rather enjoyed trying to shock me by his bloodthirsty phantasies of revenge; yet he had, after all, good reason for his hatred. He had lately, as it happened, received news of his family in Austria—nothing definite, but enough to suggest that there could be little hope of their survival. His fits of gloom became more frequent; yet his courage and resolution never failed, and his fund of natural cheerfulness could still, despite his private grief, make him a gay and responsive companion.

We remained nearly a year at Porto San Marco; during this time, the civilian population repossessed the town, and the blitzed streets and *piazzas* acquired once again a rather pathetic veneer of civilization. One day, in early spring, I noticed that a small greengrocer had re-started his business: the shattered doorway and part of the roof were underpinned with wooden posts, and the 'shop' consisted of an improvised counter backed by a few rough wooden shelves, on which were stacked piles of *finocchi* and young chicory. Shortly afterwards we discovered a wine shop, and filled our water-bottles with a sour, inferior *vino rosso*. A sudden rash of posters broke out upon the walls and house-fronts: they were mostly identical—a rather dim picture of semi-nude workers doing something strenuous, with the single word '*Ricominciamo*' printed across the top.

'So then, they begin again, the poor bastards,' remarked Kurt. 'I am sorry for them.'

Not far from our billets stood a statue of Cavour: a whiskered, frock-coated figure, with a benign, rather bewildered look upon his plump face, he had somehow managed to survive the blitz. One hand was raised in a half-questioning, half-deprecating gesture; the other clasped a stout umbrella.

'So, you see,' said Kurt, indicating with a sweeping gesture the ruined, desolate town, 'for this he is freeing Italy. I hope that now he is pleased by what he sees.'

One day at about this time Kurt and I walked out, after tea, into the *piazza*. It was a grey, rainy evening, and the ruined houses gleamed wetly in the fading light. We wandered rather vaguely up a steep, narrow street behind the church, which we had never explored before. The houses were almost all gutted; here and there fragmentary relics of occupation lingered in the ground floor rooms—a chair, a wine-flask, a broken mirror. The sunset light, struggling through the rain-clouds, shone suddenly down the street, touching the chipped and shattered stonework with a soft, yellowish brilliance. At the top of the hill, a pile of débris and a broken-down stone wall confronted us. We clambered over the rubble and boulders, and found ourselves suddenly outside the town.

A rough, desolate-looking field stretched away at our feet, sloping steeply downhill towards what appeared to be the edge of a cliff: beyond was the sea, remote and calm beneath the yellow glare of the sunset. All over the field were scattered what, for a moment, I took to be a flock of sheep; I looked again, and saw that they were stones: roughly-shaped, some flattened, some tall and more or less cylindrical, like Druidic monoliths. Curiously, we examined the nearest ones: they were inscribed with weather-worn and (to me) unfamiliar characters.

'Do you know what this place is?' Kurt asked me, a curiously dramatic note coming into his voice. 'It is the ancient Jewish Cemetery.' He peered more closely at the nearest stone. 'This one is 1673,' he said. 'You see, it is here only in old days they are allowed to bury their dead—outside the walls of the town. Here is one later, 1732: it is a larger stone, I think he is rich bloke.' Kurt spoke calmly now, in a voice deceptively matter-of-fact: I could see by his face that he was deeply moved.

We wandered slowly down the field towards the cliff-edge. Here and there, between the stones, were patches of small crimson anemones, pushing up hopefully among the drenched grass; catching the slanting sunlight, they gleamed with a strange, unearthly radiance. At the edge of the cliff were more tomb-stones: some balanced at the extreme brink, some actually projecting over the edge. Several hundred feet below, small waves lapped silently upon black, jagged rocks.

We squatted down on two adjacent stones, and lit cigarettes. Kurt was unusually silent. For some minutes neither of us spoke: we sat staring, in silence, into the sunset. A little way off, along the cliffs, was a group of Nissen huts, and in the space in front of them the occupants had got up a casual game of football. Their shouts came faintly to us, mingled with the crying of gulls. The sun, dipping beneath a cloud bank, shone out suddenly in a dying glory: and the windows of a lighthouse, on a projecting spur of cliff across the bay, caught the light with redoubled brilliance, dazzling the eyes like a magnesium flame.

Kurt remained silent. The sun was on the horizon-line: a reddish semi-circle shrinking every moment. Soon it began to get chilly: but we sat on still, unwilling to return to the desolate, unfriendly town, and to the Hospital. Looking at Kurt, slumped on his fallen stone, his big, square head bent forward, staring fixedly, gravely before him, I had a curious sense of being in the presence of something ancient, implacable, eternal. I thought back to the events of the past days: seeing them, as it seemed, through the wrong end of a telescope—impossibly diminished, Lilliputian, without significance. By comparison with Kurt, the people I had been dealing with —my fellow-privates, the N.C.O.s, the Major himself—seemed like young children or savages; half-developed, embryonic beings, floundering in the stream of an alien life. For most of us, I thought, the war—in spite of its incidental discomforts—still seemed a kind of dream, or a bad joke which we endured without quite knowing why. But for Kurt it was a tangible and serious reality, a phase in a process which had been going on all his life, and which to him was expected and familiar. Lonely, tough, self-sufficient, he seemed to me, as I watched him, perched upon the tombstone of one of his race, a kind of symbolic figure, a personification of those very forces which were responsible for my own presence here: a figure portentous and disquieting, prefiguring the shadowed, hostile future.

I spoke at last—with a self-defensive frivolity which I almost instantly regretted.

'A penny,' I said.

'A penny?' Kurt echoed. 'I do not know what you mean.'

'In England, we say: "A penny for your thoughts"—in other words, what were you thinking about?'

Kurt remained silent for some moments.

'So then, you want to know?' He paused. 'Well, I tell you: I think about this place, this cemetery where Jewish chaps like me lie buried. Hundreds of years some of them are lying: the most new stone in this field is hundred-and-fifty years old. So, if you come here in peace-time, twenty years ago, you say: "That is how they used to treat the Jews, even when they are dead they are outcast, they must bury their mother, their father, their wife or what is it, outside the walls of this nice Christian city." So—that is what you would say: and you would think "How we progress, how much better we are today, the Jewish chap can be buried now in the town, even in Christian cemetery, if he like."' Kurt paused. I was silent, embarrassed because my frivolous query had provoked him to such high seriousness.

'So then,' he went on, 'I am thinking—can you not guess? —that now the Jew is outcast again. I am thinking that perhaps we do not progress so very much, you understand?'

'Yes,' I said, 'I understand.'

Kurt said no more. We sat, smoking, for a few minutes more, the twilight deepening around us. The footballers had gone, and the whole landscape—the cliff-top, the town behind us, the little bay between the cliffs—was folded in a profound silence. I had an odd sense, sitting here in the dusk above the sea, of being, not only on the extreme verge of land, but on some remote margin of life itself. The ordinary preoccupations of our existence—food and sleep and work—seemed curiously thinned-out and immaterial. We had only to take a step or two, and we could walk over the cliff-side on to the jagged rocks two or three hundred feet below; and it seemed to me that it would require only some slight movement of the mind to precipitate me into some spiritual *néant* beyond the verges of my consciousness.

Suddenly, Kurt began to speak again.

'Ach, you are English, you do not know,' he exclaimed. 'You do not know what it is to be like I am: one who is always outcast, one who does not belong to one place, one country. I am like these poor blokes that lie under this grass, I am always outside the wall of the town. . . . I do not talk much like this, I forget for a time that I am outcast, I am happy, I enjoy the *vino*, I enjoy to make the love to a nice girl. In the Army it is easy—I have bed, I have food, I have even money. I can spend fifty lire here, hundred lire there. But after the war, when I go back to Palestine—ach, then perhaps I cannot have even these small pleasures which I have now, which make me forget. I go back with hundreds, with thousands of other Jewish chaps, I get what job I can, perhaps if I am lucky I am clerk, perhaps I work on the roads, in the fields—in any case, I am poor. But even so, if they would let me out of the Army now, I would not mind, I would be happy because I am free, because I am not soldier. Do you not think I am right?'

Kurt stopped, and, as I looked at his face, glowing momentarily in the light of his cigarette, he seemed to me, as he had seemed at other times, a kind of archetype of his race. But tonight, in this place, there was a difference: it was as if, suddenly, he were no longer alien, but indigenous: here, in this ancient graveyard of his people, beyond the boundaries of the ruined town, he seemed at last to have come into his own.

Suddenly he rose to his feet, and strolled down the path along the cliff-edge. I didn't follow him; for there was nothing at that moment, I could possibly have said. I watched his ungainly figure lumbering away into the fading light; saw him seat himself, once again, upon a fallen stone at the extreme verge of the cliff; and, as I stared into the sunset, heard his voice raised suddenly in song—that very song which I had first heard him sing, so many months ago, at Barce: a high, plangent melody which seemed now to gather to itself all the desolate melancholy of this time and place—the rainy evening light fading over the graveyard, the ruined town and the calm, illimitable sea.

It was not long after this that Kurt heard—through the Red Cross—that his mother and father and most of the rest of his family had perished in a gas-chamber at Auschwitz.

He took it so calmly that it was difficult to gauge the extent of his suffering. Outwardly he remained much the same as usual; yet I noticed that he tended, more and more, to keep to himself, and to go for long, lonely walks in the countryside. He became, too, somewhat quieter and gentler in his behaviour, and seldom gave way to his old ungovernable fits of anger;

he ceased even to rage against the Nazis—and I could guess that his hatred, now, was a thing too profound and too intimate to be expressed in words.

I was demobilized that autumn, with Group 19, and said goodbye to Kurt in Italy. We made many promises to keep in touch; I even, I remember, tried to persuade him to come to England and look for a job; alternatively, I would somehow manage, sooner or later, to visit him in Palestine; but neither of us, I think, really believed that we should ever meet again.

'No, I do not come to England,' Kurt declared flatly. 'There is now only one country where I can go, and that is Palestine. I do not think I shall be very happy, but it is my country, I shall be with other Jewish chaps, you see. As for you, I do not think you come there, even for holiday, because you would be stranger, as I am with the English blokes. We have been good friends—I have never had so great friend —and I do not forget it: but I think now our lives must go apart, isn't it?'

I wouldn't admit it at the time; but Kurt was, of course, right. Our lives, in future, were to be divided by a gulf greater than I was then able to realize. Our relationship had been one of the accidents of war—a fortunate accident; basically we had little enough in common, we were united, perhaps, only by adversity.

I have never seen him again: we write to each other occasionally, but his letters tell me little that I really want to know; he was never, at the best of times, a very good letter-writer. He is now, I believe—after a difficult spell—doing fairly well in his adopted country, where I like to think that he is having all those nice dinners and lovely girls that he used to long for, so nostalgically, in the western desert and in the ravaged cities of Italy. He, more than most people I have known, deserves his share of good fortune, and I hope that he has found happiness. Yet for me, in retrospect, he remains essentially a tragic figure; and when I think of him today, I see him always against the background of Porto San Marco, that ruined desolate town in which, during those last despondent months of the war, I came to know him best. The vision recurs of that ancient cemetery overlooking the Adriatic; and I see him once again, slumped upon the fallen tombstone in the fading twilight: the figure of an outcast, rootless and without hope, bearing about with him always, like a hidden tumour, his heritage of persecution and disaster.

Miss Wimpole

I BECAME stage-struck at an abnormally early age: I couldn't, I suppose, have been much more than five when the idea of 'the theatre' began to haunt my dreams and my waking phantasies with visions of an unattainable—and a rather unholy—delight. Unattainable, because I had never yet been taken to a play, and was given to understand that theatre-going was an almost exclusively grown-up activity; unholy, because I had formed the impression that the theatre was, by its very nature, a profoundly immoral institution. (This aura of wickedness derived, I suppose, from my nurse who, being a Strict Baptist, had been brought up to believe that playhouses were Sinks of Iniquity.) I possessed a model theatre, which kept me happily occupied for hours at a time; but my soul yearned for wider prospects, and, whenever the opportunity occurred, I would study, with an obsessional interest, the posters advertising the Pleasure Gardens Theatre, Folkestone. Sometimes, indeed, our expeditions into the town would take us past the theatre itself; and the sight of that imposing façade, with its domed roof, its pillars and its high glass doors, would fill me with such an agony of frustrated desire that I could only with difficulty be dragged away.

My first theatrical experience was, in fact, a school production of *A Midsummer-night's Dream*: it hardly counted, I felt, as a 'real' play, but it did serve effectually to whet my appetite for future delights. Meanwhile, I consoled myself with my toy theatre and, on very special and ceremonial occasions, with a small, very primitive and malodorous magic lantern.

This latter, though a poor substitute for the Pleasure Gardens Theatre, had for me a glamour all its own; indeed, it would be almost true to say that I was screen-struck before I was stage-struck. Not, of course, that I had ever been taken to a real cinema—for cinemas, even more than theatres, were a prerogative of the grown-ups, and were, moreover, in those days (at any rate in middle-class circles), universally believed to be infested with fleas and worse. No; my addiction to the silver screen was limited to those infrequent occasions when, as a special treat, I was allowed to Have the Magic Lantern.

In those days, I suppose, it must have seemed to me quite literally a thing of magic. I was always extremely slow to grasp the workings of any mechanical contrivance, and I was quite content to accept the magic lantern as something purely supernatural, like the annual visits of Father Christmas, in whom I still half-believed. The whole ritual seemed, indeed, from start to finish, to be steeped in the blackest magic: the darkened room, the flickering light upon the 'screen' (a table-cloth draped over a picture-frame), the warm sooty reek of the oil-lamp in the projector. Usually, the entertainment would be limited to ordinary lantern-slides—little strips of glass which one pushed (often upside-down, if one wasn't careful) into a slot in front of the lantern; these, in themselves, tended to be on the dull side—pictures of animals, or views of well-known places, crudely executed in violent primary colours. On exceptionally grand occasions, however (usually on my birthday, or when other children had come to tea), these rather unexciting 'stills' would be replaced by *moving* pictures—tiny celluloid films, revolving upon two reels, and worked by a handle at the side of the projector.

That these 'movies' were shown so infrequently was due chiefly, I think, to my mother's almost pathological fear of fire. She would relate the most horrifying stories of children's parties at which, so I gathered, it was quite a common occurrence for 'little-girls-in-muslin-dresses' to be burnt to death in a matter of seconds, owing to the lethal properties of something (or somebody) referred to, darkly, as the 'Sell-You-Lloyd'. I was not quite sure of what this monstrous entity consisted: but it acquired for me a quality of Gothic horror peculiarly appropriate to the darkened, mysterious atmosphere in which these sessions took place; and the excitement which I derived from the movies would be heightened to an almost intolerable pitch by the thought that, at any moment, the whole infernal machine might explode with a deafening report and envelop the room in sheets of flame—in which, of course, any little-girls-in-muslin-dresses who happened to be present would perish in indescribable agonies.

Since I was not a little girl, and since my dresses were not made of muslin, I had no fear, myself, of being involved in these threatened holocausts; none the less, I was kept at a safe distance from the smoking, whirring machine in which lurked, presumably, the terrible Demon Celluloid. Two people only were allowed (when it was a question of showing the moving pictures) to operate the dread machine—my father and my elder brother, Cecil. The whole ritual had to be conducted with infinite care and a scrupulous attention to detail; but the expected disaster never did, in fact, occur, and I acquired in due course such confidence in my father's or my brother's aptitude for propitiating the demon, that I was able to surrender myself, at last, to the undiluted pleasure of watching the films themselves.

If the ordinary, crudely-coloured slides had been fraught with magic, these moving images, cast so vividly upon the bright-lit screen, represented for me the ultimate triumph of the hermetic art: a perilous evocation of the Powers of Darkness only possible for such *illuminati* as my father and brother, who, for that matter, appeared to take such daemonic manifestations very much as a matter of course. Watching the incomprehensible antics of those mysterious familiars, I would be overcome by a pleasure so acute as to be almost unbearable: more intense by far than any I have since derived from the masterpieces of M. Eisenstein or of Mr Carol Reed. I felt, I think, in some way inextricably *involved* in what was taking place upon the screen: the bright, crude figures seemed a part of my very self, projections of my secret phantasies which were now, for the first time, made manifest, in visible form, before my waking eyes.

But such pleasures, delightful though they were, could never be more than a poor compensation for the real thing. Nothing would satisfy me, ultimately, but to go to a Real Play at the Pleasure Gardens Theatre; and at long last—shortly after my sixth birthday—I was taken to a *matinée* of *Peter Pan*.

The choice was inevitable: straight plays, as I knew, were only for grown-ups, while musical comedies and *revues*—and even the annual pantomime—were considered by my parents to be 'vulgar' if not downright improper. I would have liked, if the truth were told, to go to something rather more grown-up than *Peter Pan*; however, I was in no mood to carp, and was glad enough to have gained the *entrée*, at last, to that Temple of Iniquity in Bouverie Road West.

All the same, I was sadly disappointed by my first 'theatre'. True, I was sufficiently impressed by the place itself—the red plush and tarnished gilt seemed wholly appropriate to the Sink of Iniquity which I supposed it to be; but the performance itself by no means came up to my expectations. As the young Proust strove in vain to see La Berma through the transfiguring eye of a Bergotte, so now did I try my utmost to make Peter and Wendy and Mrs Darling correspond to my preconceived idea of what actors (and more particularly actresses) should be like. But it was no good: these were not the bedizened, Babylonish creatures proper to such a haunt of vice —they were just ordinary people, not so very unlike my own family, though they did (or so it seemed to me) speak in rather silly and affected voices. I was suitably thrilled by the flying act—though I knew, of course, that it was 'all done by wires'; as for Captain Hook, he both alarmed and fascinated me, but not much more than one of my uncles, who was in the Army, and with whom I had a somewhat similar kind of love-hate relationship.

As it happened, *Peter Pan* was my nurse's first theatre too; and she must, I think, have been somewhat surprised—and perhaps, as I was, just a little disappointed—to find that, despite its red plush and its general air of rather immoral luxury, the Pleasure Gardens Theatre was not (or at any rate not visibly) in the very least iniquitous. The stalls and dress-circle, in any case, were full of children, accompanied by their parents, aunts and nurses; nothing could have been more respectable, nor, alas, more unlike what I had expected. Nevertheless, I gloated over that *matinée* for weeks afterwards —transforming it, in retrospective phantasy, into the glamorous and sophisticated occasion which I felt that it ought to have been. *Peter Pan* had been a disappointment; but the world of 'The Theatre' itself had lost none of its power to enthrall me, and I longed for the day—alas, impossibly distant —when I should find myself, once again, wriggling with an intolerable anxiety in my plush seat in the dress-circle, and watching the gold-tasselled fringe of the curtain quivering in the sudden, apocalyptic blaze of the footlights.

As it happened, I was taken to the theatre again only a few months later—not, alas, to a play, but (somewhat improbably, considering my age) to hear a religious address by Mr Carlile, the famous Baptist preacher, for whom my nurse had a great admiration. Not surprisingly, I found the prospect rather a bore; and I resented the fact that I should be taken to the theatre on what I considered to be false pretences. The play that week happened to be Brieux's *Damaged Goods* which, at that time (it was during the first war), was being toured for propaganda purposes. The posters advertised it as being for 'Adults Only'; plainly I could never hope to be taken to it; yet I cherished a secret and inadmissible hope that the actors would somehow contrive to make a mistake, and appear upon the stage in the place of Mr Carlile. Alas! my hope was to be disappointed: when we entered the theatre, the curtain was already raised; the backcloth represented a wood—not unlike that 'Wood near Athens' which I remembered from the school production of the *Dream*. . . . Up till the last minute I continued to hope: perhaps, even yet, some delightful and scandalous mistake might occur—perhaps we had come on the wrong day, or perhaps Mr Carlile had changed his mind, or been taken ill. I waited in a tremor of excitement, expecting every moment to see a troupe of naked and iniquitous actresses trip on to the stage. . . . Presently the side-curtains bulged and parted, and a gentleman in a frock-coat stepped out in front of the footlights; he was followed by another gentleman —tall, grey-haired, his face disfigured by the scars of smallpox. . . . My heart sank: for I had immediately recognized this second gentleman, and knew him to be none other than Mr Carlile—who, alas, must have remembered his appointment after all. Soon he took up his position at the lectern and began his speech. I listened, with an excruciating boredom, as his resonant voice rolled out the incomprehensible words; perhaps a faint hope lingered, even yet, at the back of my mind, that some stray actress might appear suddenly from the wings. . . . The speech continued for what seemed hours; no actresses appeared; and at last we left the theatre—streaming out through the bright-lit foyer, placarded with exciting notices of *Damaged Goods* and photographs of the actors.

Years later, at school, I read Brieux's play: vaguely hoping, perhaps, even then, for some entrancing revelation of iniquity. Not surprisingly, I was disappointed: the play seemed to me extremely flat and tedious—almost, in fact (though not quite), as boring as Mr Carlile himself. As I read it, I was haunted by a curious sense of deprivation: surely, I thought, one of the scenes must be laid in a wood—for had not the stage been set for a woodland scene on the occasion of Mr Carlile's lecture? But no; the action of *Les Avariés* appeared to be confined entirely to doctors' consulting rooms and stuffy middle-class salons in Paris. The woodland set so considerately (if unsuitably) provided for Mr Carlile must, I reluctantly concluded, have been a 'stock' backcloth, the property of the Pleasure Gardens Theatre. My opinion of Brieux, as a dramatist, slumped abruptly; and indeed I have never, from that day to this, attempted to read him again.

It was at about the time of Mr Carlile's lecture that Miss Wimpole impinged—and I think 'impinge' is the *mot juste*—upon my life. My second visit to the theatre, though in itself a disappointment, had had the effect, none the less, of inflaming my passion for the drama; perhaps if I had been less stage-struck at the time, I might have been less impressed by Miss Wimpole; as things were, I was ripe—and indeed over-ripe —for her advent, and it was hardly surprising that I should fall an easy victim to her somewhat dubious charms.

For Miss Wimpole, unbelievably, was an Actress—or, at any rate, she had been (as my family preferred to describe it) 'connected with the stage'.... Not in the ordinary way, of course.... Quite a *lady* ... a very respectable company— *Shakespeare*, you know.... So much I gathered from the grown-ups' chatter after her first visit. I could hardly believe my ears: was it possible that I had been sitting at the same table, that very afternoon at tea-time, with a Real Actress?

Miss Wimpole had, it seemed, been introduced to my family under the most respectable auspices: my father, at this time, had developed a mild interest in theosophy, and had encountered Miss Wimpole at Adyar, the local headquarters of the cult, where he had been presented to her by none other than Dr Percy Lewis, our family doctor, whose approval was considered to be a more than sufficient guarantee of her moral character. Alas for Dr Lewis—Miss Wimpole was to prove, at a later date, to be distinctly less respectable than he had innocently supposed. For a few months, however, she remained on very friendly terms with my family, and was a frequent visitor to the house.

From the first, there was—as I gathered by judicious eaves-

dropping—something a little unusual, a little 'odd' about her.
Quite 'nice', of course; nothing that one could really take
exception to; but *queer*, you know—not quite like other
people.... Of course (said the grown-ups) she was Clever:
that would account for a good deal, quite apart from her
connection with the stage; one expected 'clever' women to
be a little unusual.... The next time Miss Wimpole came to
tea I took more careful note of her. There was, certainly,
something peculiar about her appearance: her cheeks and lips,
for instance, were very much pinker than those of most ladies
I knew. Also her clothes seemed to me unusually smart, and
she smelt very strongly of scent. I was puzzled, too, by the
fact that, although she seemed to be quite old, she behaved as
though she were a young girl of about the same age as my
sister. On the whole I liked her, though I found her a trifle
embarrassing; the mere fact that she had been an Actress
(though also, incongruously, a Lady) was more than enough
to prejudice me strongly in her favour. I should have liked to
ask her whether she had ever acted in *Damaged Goods*, but I
felt obscurely that this would not, in the circumstances, have
been altogether tactful.

Miss Wimpole was not only Clever—she was also (as we
soon discovered) Artistic. My father, tolerant on the whole
of human idiosyncrasies, had no rooted objection to this
particular one; provided that Art was confined to pictures,
he positively enjoyed talking about it, and derived, indeed,
a considerable satisfaction from exposing Miss Wimpole's
ignorance of the Barbizon school, whose work he particularly
admired. Only when the subject of music was broached did
he show any marked distaste for Miss Wimpole's artistic pre-
tensions; for the only composer whose works he really en-

joyed was Wagner, and Wagner, according to Miss Wimpole, was simply not a composer at all.

'But the man's a *barbarian*!' she would exclaim, throwing up her hands in horror. 'Chopin, yes—he is e*xquisite*' (she pronounced it like that)—'and Debussy—so delicate, so subtle! *Mais ce Wagner—ah, ça non*' (Miss Wimpole had a way of thus dropping, impressively, into French), '*ça c'est vraiment un peu trop!*'

The ballet, too, was a topic which Miss Wimpole, had she possessed more native discretion, might well have avoided in our family circle. But discretion was not one of the qualities in which she excelled.

'You haven't seen Pavlova?' she would shriek, with an exaggerated horror (she pronounced the dancer's name—as most people did in those days—with the accent on the second syllable). 'But my friend, you are missing the greatest artistic treat of the century. Do you know what a friend of mine— a very *dear* friend—said to me of Mme Pavlova?' (Miss Wimpole, by her emphasis upon the word 'dear', contrived to invest her friend with all the attributes of a passionate— though of course continent and perfectly 'respectable'—lover.) 'He said, "Eulalia" '—for this, improbably enough, was Miss Wimpole's Christian name—' "Eulalia", he said, "it is absolutely necessary that you see Pavlova—she is *Art let loose.*" '

This alarming statement flabbergasted my family, as well it might; in my own mind it evoked the disquieting image of a bejewelled and half-naked actress (who was doubtless no better than she should be) leaping suddenly from a picture-frame and waltzing, with a shameless abandon, round the dining-room table.

I realized, I think, even then, that Miss Wimpole was accorded special privileges by my family: nobody else would have been allowed to talk like that and get away with it. My father, for one, hated pretentiousness in any form ('the really well-dressed man is always the least conspicuous'); but Miss Wimpole, it seemed—for the time being, at any rate—could do no wrong. I had noticed the same kind of thing happening before: there had been Mr Watkins, the artist, for instance, and that queer Miss Shute, who sang—people whom one would have supposed to be totally incongruous in our conventional and rather Philistine social ambience; yet for so long as my father approved of them, they could behave as oddly and outrageously as they pleased. And then, all of a sudden, they would cease to come to the house, and, if their names were mentioned, my father would look displeased, and abruptly change the subject. One gathered that they were not, after all, quite the sort of people one wanted to know. Dark hints would be dropped in undertones: Mrs So-and-so, it seemed, had met Mr Watkins in Florence, and it was *said*. . . . Oh yes, it was common talk among the English colony. . . . Why, the wretched woman had actually *admitted* it, quite openly. . . . And that poor Miss Shute—so talented—one feels quite sorry for her. . . . Oh no, no doubt at all—Mrs Bellingham actually *saw* her, coming out of the Red Lion. . . . Such a pity—but of course, after that, one can hardly have her to the house, can one?

Accustomed to such abrupt—and to me largely inexplicable—falls from grace, I was convinced that, sooner or later, Miss Wimpole's turn would come. Nor, as events were shortly to prove, was I mistaken; but for the present she remained in high favour, and soon formed the habit of coming to tea with us regularly every Sunday. So high did her reputation stand, at this period, that her wildest eccentricities would, I feel certain, have been condoned and even encouraged—she might, if she had happened to feel like it, have danced the can-can in the middle of the drawing-room floor without any of us turning a hair. . . . Fortunately we were spared the can-can; but Miss Wimpole was not one to hide her light under a bushel, and it was not long before we were treated to another —and hardly less embarrassing—manifestation of her histrionic genius.

In those days it was still the custom for young ladies—and ladies not so young—who neither sang nor played the piano, to entertain the company with what were known, comprehensively, as 'recitations'. These consisted usually of sentimental or humorous verses by such poets as A.L.O.E. or Mrs Hemans, or of such popular favourites as *The Burial of Sir John Moore* or *The Leak in the Dyke*. Miss Wimpole, however, in this as in other matters, was nothing if not original: being pressed, by my mother, to 'recite', she at first affected great confusion, knitting her brows, tapping with her fingers upon the table, and in general giving the impression that, with so vast a repertoire at her finger-tips, it was a matter of infinite difficulty to select the one 'piece'—from among so many acknowledged masterpieces—which would be exactly suited to the time, the place, the quality of the *assistance* and the present state of her own so artistic and highly-strung temperament.

At last, with the air of one upon whom the spark from heaven has fallen, she rose to her feet, flashed a brilliant smile upon her expectant audience, raised her hand dramatically and announced, in ebullient tones:

'*Jabberwocky*!'

The recital which followed was one of the most unnerving experiences which, at that age, had ever come my way. I had not yet read *Alice* (I was still at the Beatrix Potter stage), and my first thought was that Miss Wimpole was reciting a poem in French; by the time she was half-way through the poem I was convinced that she must, quite suddenly, have gone raving mad. I sat through her performance in an agony of terror: fully expecting that my parents would seize upon this dangerous lunatic and put her out of harm's way. To my amazement, they made no attempt to do anything of the kind; and I could only conclude that they were too polite—or too overcome—to interrupt her ravings. At the end of the poem I sat mute with apprehension: I should hardly have been surprised if Miss Wimpole had seized a knife from the table and proceeded to stab us all to death on the spot. I could only hope that someone would restrain her in time; but instead of flinging themselves upon her in self-defence, my parents, my sister and another visiting lady broke into a round of enthusiastic applause.

'So clever,' I heard them saying, 'so *original*. . . . Sheer nonsense, of course, but so dramatic, is it not?'

Such was the success of *Jabberwocky* that Miss Wimpole, thenceforward, was seldom allowed to leave the house without giving a repeat performance. After a time I became accustomed to it—and soon, indeed, had it by heart myself. It was, I suppose, my first introduction to poetry in the true sense of the word: up till now, 'poetry' had meant for me *The Leak in the Dyke* and a number of debile, milk-and-watery verses in the 'Brown' Reading Primer—a horrid little book bound in scratchy, chocolate-coloured cloth which put one's teeth on edge when one rubbed one's nails across it.

Jabberwocky, no doubt, is a good enough poem to survive even a bad performance; but it must be admitted that Miss Wimpole's rendering, as I remember it, did more than justice to Lewis Carroll's masterpiece. From long practice, she had memorized the exact inflection proper to each phrase, and her performance scarcely ever varied. She would begin *piano, misterioso*:

' 'Twas brillig, and the slithy toves—'

(with a slight upward inflection on 'slithy'), mounting suddenly, in the second line, to a terrifying crescendo:

'Did GY-RE and *gimmm*-ble in the wabe—'

her voice, on the word 'gyre', rising to an eldritch shriek which made me jump every time I heard it—

'All *mimmm*-sy were the borogoves.
And the mome ra-a-ths outgra-a-a-be'. . . .

On the word 'mimsy' she would place her hands before her face, with the forefingers and thumbs touching, then draw them slowly apart, as though stretching a piece of elastic to its fullest extent; on 'mome raths' her voice fell once more to a guttural stage-whisper, prolonging the syllables with a lingering emphasis which evoked for me a disquieting picture of enormous hirsute monsters lurking in some miasmal jungle.

As the recital proceeded, Miss Wimpole's gestures became more and more violent and dramatic: she threw up her arms, clawed her hair, and, when she came to the part about the 'vorpal blade', would make as though to run a sword through some unseen enemy. By the time she reached the penultimate stanza she had worked herself up into a positively Bacchanalian frenzy:

'O frabjous day, callooh, callay!'

she would shriek, flinging wide her arms, throwing back her head and bursting into a sudden and prolonged peal of insane laughter.

Once I had become accustomed to it, I looked forward with immense pleasure to Miss Wimpole's weekly performance. It was a great improvement, I decided, on *Peter Pan*; and I formed a vague idea, at this time, that the grown-up plays about which I heard so much—but to which I was never allowed to go—must be like some vastly magnified and extended version of *Jabberwocky*, in which the mome raths, the slithy toves and all the rest, would appear in person upon the stage.

My father found Miss Wimpole 'interesting': she could discuss, for instance, the plays of Bernard Shaw (whom my father much admired) with great verve and intelligence, and even claimed—I should guess without a shadow of justification—to be on intimate terms with Mrs Patrick Campbell. Moreover, though so clever and artistic, she was far from being irreligious—quite the contrary, indeed. Quite apart from her interest in theosophy, she 'attended' (as she put it) the Parish Church, which was High—much too high for my father's taste; but then Miss Wimpole, being Artistic, might naturally be expected to 'revel' (as she herself expressed it) in the vestments, the music and the incense.

'I think, my dear friend,' she remarked on one occasion (and I cannot but feel that my father, though still prejudiced in her favour, must have found this form of address faintly embarrassing), 'I think we are all, *en effet*, climbing the same mountain, but by different paths—and did not our Saviour' (here Miss Wimpole's voice sank to a pious undertone) 'did not our Saviour say "In my Father's house are *many* mansions"?'

My father could not but agree: though I suspect that, even at this stage of their acquaintance, he must have viewed with a certain disquiet the possibility that he might, by some miscarriage of divine justice, find himself inhabiting, for all eternity, the same heavenly mansion as Miss Eulalia Wimpole.

The more I saw of Miss Wimpole, the more profoundly did she fascinate me. It was, I suppose, largely a masochistic attraction on my part, a fascination of horror. I was certainly not 'in love' with her; yet she loomed large in my private phantasies, an improbable, almost a supernatural figure, a *Belle Dame sans Merci* in whose vicinity I was perfectly content to palely loiter, without any particular desire for a closer or more intimate relationship. With her dark hair, her flashing eyes and her too-brilliant complexion, she possessed for me all the charm of the exotic; there was, indeed, something almost gipsyish about her, and I was reminded of the sinister yet in some way seductive fortune-teller whose highly-coloured portrait decorated the slot-machine just by the entrance to the Folkestone pier.

My nurse, alone among our household, openly disapproved of Miss Wimpole, whom she believed to be 'running after' my father; as though to confirm her statement, she would point to the fact—of which everybody was aware, though nobody quite liked to mention it—that Miss Wimpole 'made up'. This indeed was self-evident: but if further proof were needed, there was Miss Wimpole's tea-cup, with the marks of her lip-salve clearly imprinted upon the rim. Gradually, almost imperceptibly, during the next few weeks, Miss Wimpole's stock began to fall; she came to the house less often, and I noticed that my father seemed to find her less 'interesting' than formerly. She would still, on occasion, attempt to lure him into cosy little talks about theosophy; but it was plain that his own rather vapid interest in the subject was waning rapidly, and no amount of encouragement on Miss Wimpole's part seemed able to revive it. He began, in fact, to find her rather a bore; and it was noticeable that, at Sunday tea, if Miss Wimpole happened to be present, he tended increasingly to find some excuse for leaving the room as soon as the meal was over.

On one such occasion, I remember, Miss Wimpole was more than usually vivacious and self-assertive—the reason being (as she made only too clear) that an old friend of my father's, a Dr Wryford, was staying with us for the week-end. Dr Wryford was a bachelor, with a thriving practice in Harley Street—a combination which Miss Wimpole, not unnaturally, found irresistible. From the moment of her arrival, she set herself—alas, only too obviously—to ensnare him. Dr Wryford, however, was not at the best of times an easy prey for feminine wiles: a life-long misogynist, it was perfectly evident that he detested Miss Wimpole at sight; and she, poor woman, adopted the worst possible means of launching her attack. While the tea-things were being brought in, she embarked, without prelude, upon a brisk—though distinctly one-sided—discussion of the astral plane and (more particularly) of its inhabitants, with whom, to judge by the familiar tone in which she referred to them, one might have supposed her to be on terms of the closest intimacy.

Dr Wryford glared at her with an expression of scarcely concealed horror; a positivist, he had no use at all for what he was wont to refer to as 'fancy religions'. A wiser woman would have perceived her mistake in time; not so Miss Wimpole, who, nothing daunted, continued to chat familiarly about her acquaintances on the Other Side, with special reference to a personage known as 'Miss Cherokee', who, it seemed, was unusually informative about living conditions in the astral sphere, and with whom Miss Wimpole, one gathered, was in almost constant communication. Miss Cherokee, among her other talents, possessed the gift of prophecy, and quite often revealed future events to her *protégée* in the form of dreams.

'Ha!' exclaimed Dr Wryford, a spark of genuine interest appearing, for the first time, in his eyes. 'Ha! So she can tell the future, can she? D'you suppose, now, she'd have any idea who's goin' to win the St. Leger?'

Miss Wimpole shook a finger at him in playful reproof, and gave vent to what old-fashioned novelists used to call a ripple of silvery laughter.

'Ah, my friend,' she replied, with the effect of one humouring a refractory child, 'you mock at those things which are hidden from you. But never fear—one of these days your eyes shall be opened. Perhaps not on this plane, perhaps not on the next—but sooner or later the truth must be revealed to all of us. Sooner or later'—here Miss Wimpole raised one hand, dramatically, as though she were about to recite *Jabberwocky*, at the same time fixing her fellow-guest with a gaze of clairvoyant intensity—'sooner or later, my friend, all of us, yes *all* of us, I say, must be purged of the grossness which holds us captive on the Lower Plane!'

These portentous words, strangely enough, left Dr Wryford wholly unmoved. 'Ah well, I daresay you may very well be right,' he said, with a glacial politeness which would have withered anybody less insensitive than Miss Wimpole. 'Doubtless, what you say is perfectly true, but—h'm, just excuse me a moment—' Half-rising to his feet, the Doctor bent forward to assist my mother, who was attempting, unsuccessfully, to light the spirit-lamp beneath the tea-kettle.

Now the lighting of this lamp was apt to be attended, more often than not, with difficulty and even with danger. The kettle itself—a portly affair in burnished copper—was suspended from a projecting loop at the summit of a top-heavy iron tripod, fashioned in the squiggly, attenuated style of *art nouveau*; the difficulty was to remove the extinguisher from the spirit-lamp without upsetting the kettle or spilling the spirit from the lamp itself. While Dr Wryford addressed himself to this delicate task, Miss Wimpole continued to speak of the soul's purgation with the exalted air of one who inhabits, already, a higher plane, where such unworthy trifles as tea-kettles can have no place.

'Yes, my dear friend,' she insisted, 'only last night my dear Miss Cherokee spoke those very words: "Eulalia", she said—and she spoke so gravely yet so sweetly—"Eulalia, we must be purged, as by fire!"'

Scarcely were the words out of her mouth, when a sheet of blue flame leapt upwards from floor to ceiling, not a yard from where Miss Wimpole herself was sitting. My mother screamed; Dr Wryford staggered backwards, nearly knocking over the tea-table; my father leapt from his chair. For a moment it seemed that we were indeed to be purged by fire, just as Miss Cherokee had so amiably predicted; the threatened holocaust, in fact, was only averted by the gallant conduct of Dr Wryford, who, seizing a rug which lay over the back of the sofa, enveloped tripod, tea-kettle and lamp in its voluminous folds. For the next few minutes all was confusion: bells were rung, the maids were sent flying for wet dish-cloths, kettle and stove were finally removed, by brave Dr Wryford, to a place of safety in the greenhouse. When at last order was restored, Miss Wimpole was found to be sitting in precisely the same place and posture as before, not a whit discomposed by the conflagration, and looking as aloof and as maddeningly superior as the Mona Lisa herself. As Dr Wryford, shaken and sweating, resumed his seat beside her, she turned upon him a countenance whose spirituality was calculated to purge the most incorrigibly earth-bound soul of its cloddish accretions.

'And now, my dear friend,' she said, her voice taking on an ardent, a positively voluptuous intensity which caused Dr Wryford to edge cautiously away from her, 'and now let us talk about the *Horoscope*.'

It was scarcely, in the circumstances, a very felicitous suggestion; nor was its effect improved by the fact that Miss Wimpole pronounced the word with a long O, as though it were spelt 'whoroscope'. . . . I distinctly heard my father, most mild-mannered of men, make the noise which in cold print is inadequately represented as 'Tchah!' As for Dr Wryford, he turned his back, in a marked manner, upon Miss Wimpole, and began to talk to my mother about the weather. So direct a snub could hardly be ignored even by Miss Wimpole, who, for the first time since I had known her, looked flustered and 'put out'. At that moment I felt genuinely sorry for her, for I could imagine all too easily what she must be feeling. The same kind of thing was so often happening to myself: some remark of mine which, to me, seemed of epoch-making importance, would be greeted by my family with just such an air of freezing contempt. . . . Miss Wimpole, I felt, had become—at least temporarily—a kind of ally against the incomprehensible and mainly hostile world of the grown-ups; true, she remained, for all practical purposes, a grown-up herself; yet I couldn't help feeling, henceforward, that we were united, she and I, by a tacit and incommunicable bond of sympathy.

Miss Wimpole's ill-timed remark about the horoscope

became—and for long remained—one of our stock family jokes. If a tedious silence fell, or some topic had been discussed *ad nauseam*, someone was sure to say: 'And now let's talk about the *Horoscope*.' After that disastrous tea-party nobody —not even my father—could pretend to take Miss Wimpole seriously.

'*Desh* it, Henry,' said Dr Wryford, later that same evening, '*desh* it, Henry, the woman's as mad as a hatter.'

This judgment impressed me profoundly: for I had suspected, ever since *Jabberwocky*, that Miss Wimpole was a lunatic, and now my suspicion was confirmed, not merely by a grown-up, but by a doctor—and a Harley Street one at that. Presumably Miss Wimpole was harmless, or she wouldn't have remained at large; but even harmless lunatics were liable, so I had been told, to foam at the mouth, roll their eyes and—unless forcibly restrained—perform the action commonly referred to as 'throwing themselves about'. On the few subsequent occasions when I encountered her, I watched carefully for the onset of these interesting symptoms; but Miss Wimpole refused to oblige me, and I was forced to conclude that her worst paroxysms must be restricted—like 'doing Number One'—to the decent privacy of her bedroom or the W.C.

Whatever the nature of her psychosis, it was not, apparently, of a kind to attract much sympathy among her friends. Poor Miss Wimpole, in fact, was becoming increasingly unpopular. From several remarks which I overheard, it was evident that she was not quite all she had seemed: for one thing, she was extremely poor ('poor as a church mouse,' I heard my mother say). Not that my family objected in the least to her poverty; what they deplored was the pretentious manner in which she attempted to conceal it. She was not a permanent resident of Folkestone, but had come there on a prolonged visit to an old Mrs Thorogood who, it appeared, was some kind of cousin. Gossip said that Miss Wimpole, since her arrival, had been 'running up bills'—and quite large ones, too—at her relative's expense: hence her smart clothes and the general air of affluence and *chic* which she exhaled. Mrs Thorogood herself, it seemed, was not particularly well-off, but, being very charitable and rather stupid, had so far raised no objection to her cousin's extravagances.

Miss Wimpole, meanwhile, contrived to lead a remarkably gay and frivolous life for a spinster of forty-odd who hadn't (as people said of her) 'a penny to bless herself with'. She was to be seen constantly at the theatre, she went to dances at the Grand Hotel, she even hunted—or so she liked to imply. In sober fact, her 'hunting' consisted of following hounds on foot, or at best upon a borrowed bicycle; though she was careful to appear, on such occasions, in a smartly cut riding-habit and a bowler-hat—an eccentricity which caused a good deal of amusement in local society, though it can hardly have seemed so amusing to old Mrs Thorogood, who presumably had to pay for the purchase or hire of these showy accoutrements.

Once, as it happened, I was myself vouchsafed a brief glimpse of Miss Wimpole in what she was wont to refer to as her 'hunting togs'. Hounds were meeting at a farm near our country cottage—where we happened to be staying—and, as a special treat, I was allowed to attend the meet. It hadn't occurred to me that Miss Wimpole would also be present, and I was, therefore, totally unprepared for the astonishing spectacle which she presented. Attired in the smartest of habits, one hand grasping a crop, and with her bowler perched jauntily upon her head, she rode up, rather late, on a decrepit green bicycle; had she been mounted upon the finest pedigree hunter in the Shires, I could hardly have been more impressed. Spell-bound, I gazed upon this fugitive vision from afar off: I should have liked to go and speak to her, or at least wave my hand; but I was inhibited, not only by an innate shyness, but also by an obscure prescience of grown-up disapproval. Soon—all too soon—hounds moved off, Miss Wimpole was lost to view, and I was taken home to the cottage, where I became a prey to that mysterious complaint referred to by the grown-ups as 'over-excitement'. The meet, it was decided, had 'upset' me; and in future, when hounds met in the vicinity, I was kept firmly out of the way.

My cult for Miss Wimpole had always, I suppose, possessed an element of masochism, and henceforward I preferred to envisage her, habitually, *en grande tenue de chasse*—a kind of glamorous Adah Menken, an adorable tyrant of the *haute école*. For weeks after that East Kent meet, I would sing her praises constantly, till at last my mother, becoming bored by my Swinburnian rhapsodies, forbade me ever to mention her name again. As it happened—though I was not to hear of this till long afterwards—there were other reasons for my mother's veto; and, had I but known it, I was never again to set eyes upon my fair enchantress.

Miss Wimpole's popularity had (as even I had guessed) been for some time past on the wane, and my mother had continued, out of pure charity, to receive her long after she had been 'dropped' by most of her former acquaintances. A rumour had begun to circulate that she was 'fast'—and it was even whispered, in certain quarters, that she was 'no better than she should be'. My family were inclined to discredit these rumours: after all, they would insist—in answer to her detractors—after all, she had been on the stage, and one expected actresses to be a little eccentric, didn't one? And in any case, one had heard nothing really *wrong*. . . .

There came a day, however, when Miss Wimpole's indiscretions could no longer be overlooked, even by the most charitable. At one of the Grand Hotel dances she had, it appeared, danced a tango with young Mr Pettifer, the house-agent, in a manner which could only be described as downright immodest. It was bad enough for a woman of her age to dance the tango at all; but on this occasion she had been wearing a dress of unusually daring cut, and the effect had been—well, really *most* deplorable. At first my family were disposed to pooh-pooh this story which, only too probably, had been much exaggerated. Soon, however, it was confirmed by no less a person than Dr Percy Lewis, who had himself been present at the dance, and had been deeply shocked by Miss Wimpole's *outré* behaviour. He had, as he freely confessed been 'taken in' by Miss Wimpole: at Adyar she had seemed irreproachable, and he had not hesitated to introduce her to his most valued friends—including ourselves; but there came a point, after all, where a gentleman had to draw the line.

Thenceforward the gentlemen—and still more the gentle-women—of Folkestone began, with an increasing firmness, to Draw the Line, and soon Miss Wimpole was excluded from almost every house which she had formerly frequented, including our own. That disastrous tango had been her undoing; and in future, whenever her name happened to crop up, my father would look down his nose and begin to talk of something else—a sure sign that Miss Wimpole had been finally relegated to the category of persons whom one no longer 'wanted to know'.

As for myself, I felt nothing but regret for the passing of

Miss Wimpole, who, besides being a Real Actress and a (medically certified) Lunatic, possessed now the added, mysterious charm of being 'no better than she should be'. In retrospect, her personality began to acquire for me an aura of romantic nostalgia, and, just as some outlawed cult will be kept alive, by a backward peasantry, in defiance of official disapproval, so did my own cult for Miss Wimpole survive, in secret, long after my family had ceased to recognize her existence. I longed to be taken to another meet, on the off-chance that I might at least be enabled to contemplate my goddess from a distance; but even this privilege—owing to my proneness to 'over-excitement'—was now denied me. I consoled myself by studying, with a renewed interest, the posters of the Pleasure Gardens Theatre, in the vain hope that Miss Wimpole (who, after all, was an Actress) might by some miracle be appearing in a play to which, if it were considered suitable, I might persuade my parents to take me. Needless to say, no such miracle occurred; and I had to be content with cherishing in secret (and under the threat of grown-up censure) my forbidden cult of *la chasseuse maudite*. I would recite *Jabberwocky* to myself interminably, imitating, so far as I was able, Miss Wimpole's blood-curdling intonations, and no doubt deriving from this pious exercise the sort of satisfaction which a Catholic recusant, in Elizabethan times, must have obtained from his Aves and Paternosters.

On our shopping expeditions into Folkestone I would scan the passing crowd with an alert eye, hoping against hope that I might be rewarded by a glimpse of Miss Wimpole—but always in vain. Not till many months later did I hear that she had, in fact, left the town for good, not long after her immodest exhibition at the Grand Hotel. That unlucky tango with young Mr Pettifer had, no doubt, precipitated her downfall; but there were, it seemed, other reasons as well for her rather hurried departure. The details remained somewhat obscure: but it was freely rumoured that Miss Wimpole had, at long last, fallen out with her elderly relative, who had been finally compelled, chiefly from motives of economy, to Draw the Line. Miss Wimpole, it was said, had lately begun to Run Up Bills of an unprecedented magnitude—not merely for her own adornment, but (which made matters far worse) in order that she might provide a favourite curate at the Parish Church with the comforts he required. These 'comforts'— if rumour did not lie—included, rather oddly, *pâté de foie gras* and innumerable pairs of very expensive silk pyjamas. It was scarcely surprising, perhaps, if old Mrs Thorogood felt that Cousin Eulalia had presumed, ever so slightly, upon her hospitality.

There was, as I have since heard, a slight but unpleasant scandal: the curate (a very spiky young man) was removed to a parish in the East End of London; Miss Wimpole herself departed, shortly afterwards, for South Devon, where, fortunately for her, she possessed an elderly aunt who had recently invited her for an extended visit. Many years later I learned that, the aunt having conveniently died, Miss Wimpole had inherited a small legacy, and had finally made her home at Budleigh Salterton, in which salubrious resort she became (so I was assured) a well-known and respected figure in ecclesiastical circles.